THE
MISSING LINK

JO DIXON

First published 2020 by Wrate's Publishing

ISBN 978-1-9996089-8-9

Copyright © Jo Dixon, 2020

Edited and typeset by Wrate's Editing Services
www.wrateseditingservices.co.uk

A CIP catalogue record for this book is available from the
British Library.

To our children, to health and happiness

CONTENTS

Preface 7

Prologue 11

Freak of Nature 13

Provence... 22

Listen.. 30

Joint Pains.. 34

Tangles 38

Crab Apples 42

Second Chance... 46

Sick Chicks and Ducklings 52

Adding Salt to Crisps... 62

Hysterical Illness.. 71

The Fall... 74

Hypoglycaemia... 80

Café Game 84

Empty Calories... 91

Black Diary... 100

Beriberi 105

Seesaws.. 116

Puzzles... 122

Red Rice 136

Thiamine – Essential for all Living Things............. 141

Breath Tests 155

More Marvellous Facts About Thiamine 159

CONTENTS

Mad Bowel Disease...174

Life as a Chorister 188

Dementia Friend..192

Resveratrol...200

Ten Per Cent Human...212

Thiaminases...221

Mark in the Sand...231

A Novel Approach 238

Enterohepatic Circulation...255

Malrotation Case 267

Abnormal Glucose Metabolism 273

Pre-Dementia Screening..282

Dysphagia Lusoria 288

Final Battle...291

Life's Ups and Downs 296

Postscript 304

References... 306

Bibliography.. 313

Acknowledgements.. 314

About the Author... 316

Preface

IN THE YEAR 2012, at the age of 43, I sat down and wrote a living will, expressing my wishes for end of life care. I was a mother, a wife and I had a successful career as a hospital consultant. I had everything to live for yet I was certain that my life, as it was, was not worth living. Contained within the pages of this book is an autobiographical account of the dementia-like illness that afflicted me during this time. There was no obvious cure. For a while it confounded many people in the medical profession, but with the help of friends and colleagues, I eventually found a treatment that improved my symptoms. Initially it felt like I had received a miracle drug. As I recovered, I tried to find out why it had been effective. The illness had been a mystery, but why the treatment worked was even more of an enigma.

Dementia affects more than one in 20 people over the age of 60, and one in six over the age of 80. There are currently over 40 million people living with Alzheimer's dementia in the world.[i] The numbers have been predicted to rise at a frightening rate in the next 30 years, to 100 million.[ii] There are 850,000 people with dementia in the UK and Alzheimer's dementia is the most common form of the disease. In this type, abnormal proteins called amyloid plaques accumulate in the brain and brain cells become unable to send chemical signals and eventually die.

Vascular dementia occurs when narrowed blood vessels limit the oxygen supply to parts of the brain. It is often seen in patients following strokes, which happen if the large blood vessels are narrowed, but it may also occur if the small vessels are occluded. Other types include a mixed picture (a combination of the above), or Lewy body dementia, which may be associated with Parkinson's disease. Dementia can also occur in patients who are immunosuppressed, such as with HIV, and in people who have suffered multiple head injuries, such as professional sports players.

Mild cognitive impairment is a term used for people with slight difficulties with memory. There is an unexplained overlap between people with this condition and mental illness, depression and anxiety, and there are many unanswered questions. Some people with mild cognitive impairment will progress to having dementia, but not everyone.

In the course of my career, I have seen new diseases emerge and treatments discovered. For instance, patients with HIV (human immunodeficiency virus), the virus that leads to AIDS (acquired immunodeficiency syndrome), can now take drugs that dramatically reduce their viral load to undetectable levels, meaning they are able to live normal lives. I have seen successful cancer screening programmes introduced, such as for bowel cancer, which can detect early signs of the disease, as well as pre-cancerous polyps, which if treated can prevent cancer developing in the first place. Medical progress has changed the outcome for patients with these conditions.

Sadly, this is not the case for other illnesses. For many years we have known that viruses can cause hepatitis (literally inflammation of the liver). There are a few other causes – mainly drugs, autoimmune and inherited conditions. Viral hepatitis A was recognised during World War II. It is spread through the faecal-oral route. Viral hepatitis B was discovered in 1965. There are now vaccines available against both hepatitis A and hepatitis B. Viral hepatitis C was discovered in 1989. There was another strain that wasn't due to viruses A, B or C – the so-called 'non-A non-B non-C' hepatitis. In the late 1980s, I learnt that fat accumulating in the liver was thought to cause it – it wasn't a virus. Back then it was called syndrome X, and it was also known as non-alcoholic fatty liver disease. Alcohol can also cause fat to accumulate in the liver, but these particular patients weren't drinkers. The condition fascinated me.

Metabolic syndrome was a term first used in the 1970s to describe a cluster of diseases occurring together: obesity, diabetes mellitus, high blood pressure, high blood lipids, high uric acid leading to gout, in addition to fatty liver. It was found that these were risk factors for heart disease and strokes. Once it was recognised that these were all associated with insulin resistance – insulin was being produced, but the body was no longer responding to it – metabolic syndrome became known as syndrome X.

Dementia is now the fifth leading cause of death.[i] Despite large amounts of research and progress in this field, the exact cause remains unknown. There are no known cures. It is possible to identify risk factors: obesity, diabetes, smoking and excess dietary sugar – especially in drinks.[i] It is also possible to slow progression with treatments, but as these don't target the underlying cause they eventually stop working. Why do only some people with mild cognitive impairment progress to dementia? Is early dementia reversible? Is mild cognitive impairment a symptom with many causes, one of which is dementia? There are other fascinating facets to this disease, such as its high prevalence in women (1.6 times as many women than men are diagnosed with it).[i] Likewise, we do not know the cause of metabolic syndrome. We know contributory factors but not the actual underlying problem.

In my case, I have completely recovered. I had a moderate dementia-like illness and I found the cure, and the underlying disease process – metabolic syndrome of the brain.

Prologue

I FELT LOST, PETRIFIED AND GLUED TO THE SPOT. I was on a morning ward round, reviewing patients' drug charts with a colleague, when I suddenly found myself unable to remember where I was. I could tell that I was on a ward, as there were patients around me, and I knew I was a doctor, so I rationalised that it was most likely my ward. So why didn't anything look familiar? I couldn't even remember how I had got here. Like a sheep I followed my colleague, and after a while everything seemed familiar again.

The experience left me terrified. I was astounded by the variability: one minute I had been in control the next I hadn't a clue. Despite this experience I still worked. With no diagnosis I thought that maybe my mystery illness was all in my head. After all, my tests had all come back normal. I had lost the ability to reason with myself. I didn't know – I didn't know anything any more.

Freak of Nature

FOR A COUPLE OF YEARS I HAD NOTICED that I had a tic: an intermittent flicker of the lower eyelid. It was irritating when it happened, as it felt as though I was winking at everyone. I would keep a finger over one eye to stop it constantly twitching. However, that looked even stranger, as though I was waving at passers-by, or, even worse, as if I was trying to keep my eye propped open. It was infuriating. It was usually an indication that I was becoming exhausted. Unfortunately, this was occurring more frequently.

I had been at a meeting in London all day and knew that I was tired. I had winked at everyone on the train on the way to the college. Trying to stop my eyelid from scrunching up distracted me from the business being conducted, and I felt as though I had saluted all the consultants around the table. The whole day had been a disappointment. I couldn't believe I hadn't been better prepared.

Together with colleagues, I had organised some major changes to national recruitment for junior doctors. I was the designated spokesperson and the meeting was primarily arranged to inform the panel of the progress that had been made. But as I sat at the table, with the minutes in front of me and the other doctors gazing in my direction, I hadn't been able to remember any of the details. The dates, figures and numbers vanished from my mind, as though they had been permanently erased. I was lost.

As I travelled home on the packed train from Liverpool Street, I desperately tried to piece together the events of the day. I realised that I couldn't even remember the action of reading the minutes. My mind was blank. It was baffling. I always read the minutes before a meeting and prepared extremely thoroughly. This made no sense.

It was then I noticed the fasciculations (muscle twitches) in my legs. Initially these had occurred in my right thigh and then they affected my left leg. I had raced to the station to get the last cheap seat on the 16:30 train, before rush hour officially started. Sitting in the carriage at a table with three other passengers, my legs became jumpy and restless. After moving them slightly the fasciculations would stop, only to restart when I rested my legs back on the couch. Shifting my legs without kicking the man opposite was difficult. If I put my hand on my skin I could feel the irritating repetitive twitches. I pinched my legs hard to make them briefly cease firing, but within seconds the flickering started afresh.

I then began to experience maddening 'restless legs' at night. At first I didn't know that was what they were. A friend's father had recently died of motor neurone disease. I knew I shouldn't ignore what could possibly be a potentially serious symptom. I had seen patients in the latter terrifying stages of the disease, but I wasn't sure about the early signs. I read up on them. Most people present with the following symptoms: muscle weakness, wasting of the muscles, fasciculations and cramps. Over time, these progress to falls and then weakness of the respiratory muscles, causing a cough. It was concerning until I read that motor neurone disease seldom presents with fasciculations alone. I was relieved, but what was causing the restlessness?

Often at bedtime I would read up about different conditions, becoming an undercover sleuth. There is no better incentive than one's own health. I started to review the symptoms I had experienced. There were many strange ones, and I was aware that many of them were difficult to explain. I admitted to myself that there was actually no point in telling anyone about them, as I felt sure no one would listen. More than ever, I was certain that I would be told I was just stressed.

I went over my other random symptoms. I had suffered with reflux for more than 20 years. I recalled the bouts of heartburn I had experienced when I worked in Cambridge as a hospital registrar. After this there had been the recurrent laryngitis and, latterly, recurrent chest infections. The first episode of pneumonia was when I had been pregnant with my second baby, 11 years earlier. The GP hadn't believed me then and I had resorted to treating myself. It was two weeks before my elective caesarean section and I didn't want to be unwell during and after the birth. It wasn't normal to have chest infections so frequently. Eventually, I recognised that the recurrent cough was actually repeated bouts of aspiration. I slept effectively sitting up, and resorted to propping myself up in the bed periodically through the night whenever I woke with a choking sensation or heartburn.

I had experienced other vague symptoms for years: the most prominent one being fatigue. I had always been extremely fit, but now I was finding it difficult to walk up hills or even stairs. I also had extremely dry, straw-like hair. Children who didn't know me commented that I looked strange, and I agreed – I thought that from the shoulders up I resembled a scarecrow. I had noticed over the past four years that I hadn't been able to eat as much as previously and, assuming that this was just middle age creeping up, it had not crossed my mind that generally people tend to gain weight as they age. In any case, I was only just forty.

Following large meals, I then experienced a few episodes of blockage. In fact, for most people the meal would not have been considered large – just normal or even small! Afterwards, I would be awake all night experiencing an unpleasant sense of obstruction. Of course, I had blamed this on the four caesarean sections I had undergone. The last section had been complicated by bladder perforation. I was convinced that adhesions were the most likely explanation.

During the past year, I had developed another bizarre symptom, namely difficulty swallowing food, especially fresh bread. There are some symptoms that can be exacerbated by stress, such as chest pain, palpitations, breathlessness and headaches. There are some that may be due to underlying malignancy, so-called red-flag signs, particularly if associated with weight loss. As a doctor who specialised in gastroenterology, I knew that dysphagia (swallowing difficulty) is not a symptom to be ignored, but I was still sure I would be told the cause was stress. I arranged to have an endoscopy and was surprised to learn that it wasn't quite normal. There was a 'distortion' in the mid oesophagus and it seemed to 'twist', causing a slight narrowing. The following day, I had a barium swallow X-ray test. I remember being alarmed by how quickly it was arranged. The barium swallow wasn't entirely normal either. I read the report:

'Cervical oesophagus normal. Slight focal indentation of the left side of the thoracic oesophagus at the level of the aortic arch. This could be due to an aberrant right subclavian artery but there is no significant posterior indentation of the oesophagus to confirm this...'

I had a normal upper gullet, but then there was a kink, a dent, in the middle of my gullet, which was presumably causing the sensation of food sticking. My gullet appeared to 'twist', and at that point it seemed to narrow. The radiologist made a further comment at the end of the report:

'Slight distortion of the oesophagus at the level of the aortic arch. The swallow appearances are not typical of an aberrant right subclavian and, as you know, it is very unusual for an aberrant right subclavian to cause significant dysphagia.'

It was apparently suggestive of a congenital abnormality of the major arteries from my heart – an 'aberrant right subclavian artery'. Normally, this artery arises from a vessel on the right of the aorta to supply the right arm. Mine seemed to arise from the left side of my aorta, crossing the gullet from behind and heading towards my right arm in a circuitous route. This caused an indentation in the gullet midway through the chest, which is what the endoscopist had judged to be 'not quite right'. However, the radiologist reporting my barium swallow had indicated that it wasn't characteristic of an aberrant right subclavian artery, as this rarely causes swallowing difficulties. He had seemed to dismiss my case, mainly because it was rare, but also since he couldn't demonstrate a significant posterior compression of my gullet. There was another brief line on the report:

'D-J flexure lies to the right of the midline.'

The barium swallow had also shown that my duodenum, or rather the end of my duodenum as it becomes the small bowel (jejunum), was to the right of the middle of my abdomen. I remembered the radiologist questioning me about my symptoms, not really the swallowing problems, but my other complaints.

Back at home, I researched the abnormal position of the duodenum and worked out that I probably had both an aberrant right subclavian artery, which caused the swallowing difficulties, and a malrotation of my small intestines, which was responsible for the recurrent blockages, heartburn and repeated aspiration. These two congenital abnormalities would certainly explain the majority of my symptoms, even if the presentations were slightly unusual. Malrotation usually presents within the first few weeks of life with vomiting and failure to thrive. When had it first presented in me? I tried to remember how long I had suffered with symptoms.

★

Jersey in the summer: beaches, cows and giant tortoises humping in the zoo. It was a fun holiday, but eating late again I developed another episode of pain. I was away with Mum, Mum's partner and my sister, Becky.

I was 14 years old. Becky and I were free to explore the beachside hotel and the swimming pools in the day, before gathering together as a family for dinner, either in a local restaurant or the hotel. Fortunately, that night we had dined in the hotel's grill restaurant, and I was able to escape back to my room. After a few mouthfuls I suddenly lost my appetite completely. Having excused myself from the table, I lay curled up in bed. The pain had started like a wave of nausea and I knew I wouldn't be able to eat any more, even though minutes earlier I had started eating my meal with great gusto. These episodes of central abdominal pain followed the same pattern, starting gradually and then becoming really intense within a few minutes, like a hot poker being pushed through my belly button until I was left exhausted and numbed. Often they would last several hours and, thinking back, the pains were always related to eating. They also seemed to happen when I was most hungry and ate quickly on an empty stomach.

After each episode, I always vowed to see a GP. Of course, I never did. As far as I was concerned, the doctor would be dismissive and make me feel stupid. There had been a time when these pains had occurred regularly, as often as each week. My mother would take Becky and me swimming each Sunday after church and my father would stay home to cook lunch. I loved my Sunday roast; it was the best meal of the week and I was always ravenous after doing lengths or splashing in the pool for an hour. Within a few minutes of eating, though, I would lose my appetite and complain of abdominal pains. It was blamed on me drinking too much chlorinated water. My problems became comparatively unimportant when I was nine and my father left the family home to start a new family. I didn't mention them to my mother any more. She had enough to worry about – she had to start working again and she was often unwell, too.

As a teenager, I did see my GP about my foot pains. Stupidly, I didn't mention the abdominal symptoms. He told me I had chilblains and advised me to wear solid, unfashionable shoes. He said I should try to set a new trend. I was made to feel I had wasted his time.

In my twenties, shortly after starting as a registrar in Cambridge, I saw a patient who had undergone a total small bowel resection for bowel ischaemia (lack of blood supply causing damage), secondary to malrotation. He had almost no small gut remaining and you need at least 60cm to be able to absorb nutrients. He had to be treated with total parenteral nutrition (liquid food pumped directly into his blood) via a large vein, usually in the chest or neck. He would be dependent on this for life unless a small bowel transplant, still pioneering surgery even now, was an option. I remembered wondering why this 'intestinal malrotation' hadn't been picked up earlier, and briefly considered whether malrotation with volvulus (twisting of the gut) explained my recurrent abdominal pains. I very quickly dismissed this notion as ridiculous, feeling foolish for even thinking about it.

Since then I had seen many GPs about various problems: reflux, indigestion, abdominal pains, nausea and chest infections. Each time I would be prescribed a pill and sent on my way. These were all common problems and there was nothing alarming to report or find.

I explained the results of the barium scan to my mother, who confirmed I had been admitted to hospital a few hours after birth with recurrent vomiting, before being discharged without further investigation. Mum had been reprimanded for overfeeding me. I had presented with symptoms as a neonate, but the diagnosis had been missed.

★

Historically, the term dysphagia lusoria, literally a 'freak of nature', was used to describe the swallowing difficulties encountered with posterior compression of the oesophagus by the abnormally positioned subclavian artery. The radiologist was correct. This artery doesn't very often cause dysphagia, but there are cases, particularly in patients who have lost weight. My reading suggested that it seemed to be increasingly recognised. The original description was by a doctor named

Bayford[1], who at the time was an apprentice surgeon. Bayford[1] discovered this abnormal artery during the autopsy of a lady called Jane Fordham, who had 'obstructed glutition' and over a period of years effectively starved to death, being unable to swallow anything for the last three years of her life.

I was stunned to find out in my forties that I had congenital abnormalities. I had associated these sorts of problems with abnormal hearts or heart valves. In my mind, congenital abnormalities were conditions that you were aware of from birth, and which required infrequent visits to a specialist for monitoring. These problems would at some stage require intervention, often in the form of major surgical correction. It was strange to think that I might fit into this bracket. I had always thought I would find out I was special, perhaps that I had an amazing, still-to-be-discovered skill, or that I was in fact famous by birthright. Alas no. In reality, I was a freak. I was defective. Imperfect.

I made a conscious decision to manage my condition conservatively by eating frequent, small meals, chewing slowly and avoiding eating late at night. I undertook not to eat after 6 pm and to eat my main meal early in the day. I also vowed not to drink any alcohol, which seemed to make my symptoms worse. As I barely drank at all these days, it wasn't a great loss. I certainly didn't want to undergo an operation.

Should I have recognised that there were problems earlier? I knew that recurrent chest infections weren't normal, but when did something that just happened regularly change from being a nuisance to indicating something more sinister?

Provence

2010

'YOU OK?' MATTHEW, MY HUSBAND, texted.

'I'm fine,' I replied. 'Just returning bicycles.'

I received a series of text messages updating me.

'Cottage fantastic.'

'Lovely shallow bay.'

'Boys happy messing around on surfboard.'

'See you Sunday.'

It was a crazy plan. That summer, my sister and I had decided to go on a cycling holiday to Provence, but the dates clashed with the already booked family holiday to Scotland. I worked out a plan to fly out to Provence with Becky and then jet back to Glasgow to meet up with Matthew and the family on the Sunday. I had been looking forward to spending time with my sister and was upset at the thought of having to cancel, as I'd had very little time to myself since the children were born. This was the only way it would work.

Becky and I had enjoyed a similar holiday the previous year. That time we had rented a room in a hotel in Avignon, close to the station. We found the cycle hire place relatively easily, bought maps and started touring the area, always returning to our hotel at night. That was until we were a little over ambitious and cycled to Gordes in the Luberon hills. It was a steep climb to finally reach the village, and we didn't stop for lunch until four in the afternoon. There was a piano concert being performed on the terraces that evening and we made a spontaneous decision to find a room for the night and stay to watch it. We bought dresses, footwear (the cycle shoes did not set off the dresses) and toothbrushes and felt rather pleased with ourselves over our ingenuity, until the locals began to arrive with blankets. No one else was wearing a summer frock and sandals. We were left to shiver along to Beethoven.

The cycle back to Avignon the next day, past the lavender-laden valley of the Sénanque Abbey, was breathtaking. Back at the hotel, the manager was pleased to see us. He was worried that we had been involved in an accident. We thought we had been clattering in and out of the hotel each evening with our two bicycles and helmets relatively unnoticed, but apparently not so. It had been an adventure and we promised each other that we would repeat the experience annually. After all, both Becky's husband and Matthew managed to have several trips away every year pursuing their hobbies. Matthew had encouraged me to go.

This year we stayed in an old hotel in Villeneuve-lès-Avignon, over the bridge across the Rhone from Avignon. Villeneuve-lès-Avignon, which had once been connected to Avignon by the famous Pont d'Avignon (Pont St-Bénézet), had its own castle. The hotel was built of limestone, with lavender-grey shuttered windows and a crypt-like entrance hall, so it felt like walking into a cave. There were pillars and nooks, but also several open-plan stairways with iron bannisters, which gave the hotel a light, airy feel. It was an interesting building architecturally and beautifully decorated with local artwork.

We cycled to various towns to the south and west. These included Arles and Saint-Rémy-de-Provence, where we followed the art trail of Vincent van Gogh. We saw the bright yellow walls of the café depicted in his painting *Café Terrace at Night* and the view from his asylum window in St Remy. Up close, his course brushstrokes were scrawls, but overall his picture was inspirational. We then pedalled up the steep, winding hillside to the abandoned medieval town of Les Baux-de-Provence.

We decided on our destination each morning in the same café overlooking the market square, whilst sipping coffee and munching on pastries. The waiter was interested in our adventures and helped us plan a couple of routes. On the last day we decided to visit the pretty market town of Uzès. Becky's French was better than mine and she found out from the waiter that the road there was flat. I heard them discussing a 'plateau'. As this was the last day of our trip, we had to be back early to return the hired bikes. Unfortunately, some of the details must have been lost in translation, as the route included some of the steepest inclines and descents of the entire trip. It was flat on top of the limestone plateau, but as soon as there was a river the road dipped into deep ravines. We took pride in our achievements and acknowledged that we must be fitter, as the previous year we would have walked up many of these hills. This year there was much complaining, panting and the singing of motivational songs, but we completed all the ascents. We were rewarded with a late lunch in the Place aux Herbes, in the centre of the town next to the fountain, where we were seated under the welcome shade of the plane trees.

There were some funny incidents. Becky was impressed by how friendly everyone was. The villagers were always waving at her. I thought it was slightly odd. I knew that Becky was better than me at French, but the people greeting her didn't know that. She *was* very attractive; in her early forties, with shiny dark brown hair and petite features, but it still didn't make sense.

Then the locals started calling out to her 'casquette!'

Becky was mystified, but joked that they must have confused her with a well-known Tour-de-France cyclist or even a pop star. She waved back, enjoying her rapid rise to fame. Suddenly it dawned on her. In fits of giggles, she called to me to stop and wait. She took her cycle helmet off and put it back on the right way round. The helpful villagers had been trying to tell her that she had been cycling along with her helmet on back to front!

Then there was the time I had to stop pedalling and wait for her. I usually took the lead, mainly because her sense of direction was dreadful. It was a flat road and there had been no turnings, therefore it was difficult to understand how my sister had fallen so far behind. I stopped and waited patiently. After a while I decided to phone her. She told me hurriedly that she was fine and that she would be along in a few minutes. I waited by the side of the road in the hot sun, listening to the breeze in the trees, rustling grasses and chirping crickets. Twenty minutes later, there was still no Becky and I was beginning to get worried. Eventually she appeared, looking really pleased. She had stopped to speak to a 'lovely' couple. They were lost and pulled up their car to ask Becky for directions. She had carried out the entire conversation in French. This was incredible, as she was notoriously shy, and then there was her map reading! I was amazed. We completed the day's trip without any further delays.

That evening, we were heading out for supper when Becky suddenly disappeared behind a pillar in the hotel.

'Have they gone?' she whispered.

'Who?' I replied, baffled. Becky was behaving strangely.

'Shhh!' She looked horrified.

I lowered my voice. 'What's going on? Are you going to tell me?'

An elderly couple had just arrived at the reception. They left the hallway and Becky came out from her hiding place and whisked me away to the safety of the restaurant, where she revealed that the French motorists she had helped were staying in the same hotel. I couldn't understand the problem. Becky had enjoyed speaking to them in French. At that moment she cringed, her natural shyness returning. The lovely French couple had been talking to the receptionist. Although Becky never told me what they were discussing, I had my suspicions. We spent the rest of our stay trying to avoid meeting them on the exposed stairway.

Becky was always the healthy one. I was definitely fitter, but seemed to have suffered from every childhood illness going, whereas my sister managed to develop the immunity without having to go through any of the discomfort associated with the disease. I was quicker on the bike, but over the last few days had developed an irritating cough. It was something that had been happening a lot lately.

Getting everything ready for the cycling holiday and then the family trip had been a major organisational feat. Work had been particularly stressful, as I had been coordinating changes to the junior doctors' rotas. Having been instrumental in overseeing the project, I felt responsible for ensuring everything ran smoothly. I'd also tried to fit in an eye test for me as well as dental appointments for the children. I couldn't believe it when the optician told me to have my cholesterol checked, as I had cholesterol deposits in the vessels in my eyes.

I thought this notion was utterly ridiculous. I had a healthy diet and lifestyle and no family history of heart disease. I was the least likely person to need cholesterol-reducing medicine!

'If it isn't broken don't fix it!' I muttered. This was Matthew's mantra and it suited my situation. I was too busy for this nonsense.

The family trip included a week in a cottage on the coast and a second week on a skippered yacht. I did not trust Matthew to pack for the two weeks, nor did I trust the children not to unpack and disorganise the holiday gear. I came up with the ideal solution and packed before I left for Provence, putting the luggage in the roof box and locking the pod. I gave the keys to the au pair for safekeeping.

It was really good to be reunited with my family again. I had the feeling that I had been missed and was appreciated once more. I flew directly to Glasgow and Matthew met me at the airport, leaving the children with the au pair. He proudly announced that he had brought my new bike with him to Scotland. I couldn't deny having cycling clothes, but I had purposely left behind my cleat shoes, which fix your feet to the pedals. Unfortunately, Matthew had remembered them for me.

'Drat!' I said under my breath, whilst smiling in mock appreciation. He was determined I would try using cleats, because it apparently makes cycling easier. I was determined that fixing your feet to the pedals only made one thing easier – and that was falling off. I practised on the steep hill climbing away from the shallow bay. Tom, our nine-year-old son, cycled up with me offering guidance. I had a few tumbles and almost gave up. The trick was to make sure that the cleat fastener released easily. Once I was confident I could unfix my feet, I agreed it made going uphill less of a challenge.

The first week, Matthew and I went for a cycle ride every morning before the children woke up. I continued my early morning coffee habit, this time in cafés along the West Coast of Scotland. We explored the area together in the afternoons and sampled the local food every evening. Matthew had discovered that the shrimp man did his rounds on Tuesdays, so he arranged for a delivery. Upon returning to the cottage on the said day, we were surprised to find a plastic supermarket bag on the doorstep full of large prawns. The whole family set to preparing for a feast. Two big pans of water were boiling on the hob as Matthew fetched the first prawn out of the bag. Suddenly there was a yelp and he started a jig in the kitchen. He is not renowned for his moves on the dancefloor and looked really strange. Edward thought it was hilarious and joined in, until I realised that Matthew had a large crustacean clamped onto his index finger.

The rest of the week was less frantic, with mountain bike trails, visiting the beavers, watching the waders in the estuary and investigating the numerous stone circles. It really was a beautiful area. Looking out to the Paps of Jura, it was possible to see the inlet between the isles where the whirlpool, named 'the Corryvreckan', had wrecked ships. The yacht we had chartered was named after this infamous area. Tom was concerned it meant certain catastrophe.

There wasn't enough room in the car for everyone including the au pair, so whilst I drove up the coast to Oban to get the ferry to Kerrera, Matthew and the au pair cycled. I reflected on the fact that there wouldn't be many people arriving for a week on a 64-foot yacht by bicycle.

I have to admit that we were a slightly unusual family. Cycling had become a major feature in Matthew's life; he had even taken a bicycle skiing. Arriving in the Portes du Soleil for our family ski trip the previous year, I had commented that we were the only people in Morzine with a bike on the back of the car. After a ride to the col, he had then remarked, with a hint of disbelief in his voice, that it was slippery!

That was the last time we went skiing. It had been a difficult trip, not just because of the brown snow, as the children had called it, or the fact that there was grass visible under the trees (a definite sign that the snow conditions were poor), but because I had been suffering from significant bouts of indigestion. I had felt so full and decided to avoid overeating. I purposefully reduced how much I ate in the evenings and minimised my alcohol intake. It was strange how my symptoms were always worse on holidays.

While away, I kept up my routine of sleeping propped up, which I'd been doing for the past two years. In Provence, I used my suitcase with rolled-up quilts acting as a mound of pillows. The hotel staff insisted on remaking the beds each day, however, taking apart my careful arrangement. Becky and I laughed as I re-rolled the quilts each night. She was used to her eccentric sister, but it wasn't until she made a comment that I realised how far from normal my behaviour was. Sleeping on a boat was even more of a challenge. I hadn't really thought this through; there was no headroom on the bunk to allow me to sleep propped up, so it made for a very uncomfortable week. I took to sleeping on the floor, using a pillow and a pile of clothes to achieve the desired effect.

Listen

IN MY CAREER AS A CONSULTANT, I no longer carried the arrest bleep or worked a regular night shift, but I still attended emergencies in the evenings. It was the best and the worst part of the day. The workload predictably increased at 6 pm each evening. The patients typically saw their GPs in urgent slots late morning; they were then referred by their GPs, and by early afternoon were waiting in the Emergency Department to be seen. As a result of a four-hour target in the ED they had to be moved on, usually to our department. Teams tended to finish their shifts at this time of the day, so by six there was an inevitable backlog in the Acute Medicine Unit.

Things had changed since the days of my training. Juniors were protected now and worked a maximum of 48 hours per week. Although this was good for their health and social life, I felt that hard work never killed anyone. After spending three years in hospital, either working or studying for exams as a junior doctor, I had been amazed to rediscover the seasons. Blossom was beautiful. I had almost forgotten the different shades and timings, as each type of tree exhibited its own glories. I had taken it for granted each year until I had been banished to the basement for my years of residency.

The 48-hour working week has been achieved by creating shifts of doctors. Where once there would have been a team, now there are individuals. Where once there was a hierarchy of experience and an inverse level of learning, now there are workplace-based assessments – a tick-box exercise so that the juniors can demonstrate they have seen a variety of cases. I had learnt by seeing as many as 30 patients every time I was on call for a 24-hour shift, which happened every third day. Despite working overnight, I reviewed my patients every day so I would know if the furosemide I had administered the evening before for heart failure had worked, or whether my diagnosis had been correct when the test I ordered showed a pulmonary embolus. I regularly worked over 80 hours in a week, but I learnt from the successes, experiencing a real sense of achievement and pride; I also learnt from the mistakes.

As a junior doctor in my twenties, I was stuck in the hospital every second or third night. Gradually, as it was recognised that this system was barbaric, the on-call frequency was reduced to every sixth night or less. This obviously meant there were fewer junior doctors in the hospital overnight, even though the workload was increasing. I did most of the really antisocial weeks of night shifts prior to having a family. I'm not sure how I would have managed to have four children whilst working the gruelling rotas that the registrars presently had to work.

Back then the majority of work was general medicine. We saw and treated every adult that didn't require surgery or delivery. It was fantastic. Unfortunately, it is these skills – the ability to manage all medical emergencies – that mean general medics now do the brunt of the night shifts, so it's not an attractive proposition, especially for my junior colleagues with families. As a result of my training, I had learnt that the most important lesson to pass on to trainee junior doctors was the need to pay attention to what the patient says, and to take a thorough history.

'Listen to your patient, they will tell you the diagnosis.'

This phrase had been borrowed from Sir William Osler. He changed medical training in the 19th century by ensuring his students learnt on the ward rather than in the lecture theatres. I would tell my juniors of a particular patient of mine who told me the diagnosis after presenting with sudden onset double vision, abdominal pain and vomiting. They had learning difficulties, which meant it was even more important to communicate effectively. The double vision meant the patient had been referred by his GP as having suffered a stroke, but together with the abdominal pain it was a rather odd presentation. He was also clearly breathless at rest.

'Is no' a stroke! I tell 'im. Is not!' the patient said. 'Is those neboozers.'

He was insistent, trying to touch me, to reach out. 'Is those neboozers wot done it. Is no' a stroke,' he declared again, clearly desperate to get his message across.

The man was hunched up on a chair with his eyes tightly shut. I ascertained that the vision was not 'double', as he wasn't seeing two images. Rather his vision was blurred. When he opened his eyes, they were red.

Enquiring about his other symptoms, particularly his breathing, the patient admitted that he had been struggling to breathe for several days and had increased his nebulisers. In fact, he had increased all his nebulisers, including the ones that should only be given four times a day. His nebuliser mask had not fitted well and he said that the mist had blown directly into his eyes. He was quite clear that the blurred vision occurred after using the nebulisers. In fact, he had been using these almost continuously. He then developed abdominal pain and vomiting, as a secondary event to the blurred vision.

I asked him to close his eyes and gently pressed on his eyeballs; it felt as though he had marbles in the sockets. He had in fact developed acute glaucoma and this was secondary to the drug he had inadvertently overdosed on in the nebuliser. At medical school, I had been taught that acute glaucoma could present with abdominal pain and vomiting, and that without urgent treatment visual loss could occur. Immediate referral to the ophthalmologist saved this patient's sight. He was right all along – the nebulisers had caused his problems. The patient had told me the diagnosis and fortunately I had listened to him.

Joint Pains

MY SYMPTOMS INTENSIFIED AS I LOST WEIGHT. There had to be a connection between these abnormalities. Saddened by the discovery of congenital defects, but now even more determined, I tried to solve the riddle.

I had been a size 12, weighing 60kg, when I went on the cycling holiday with Becky. Upon my return, I became more active. I even started running after being encouraged by Matthew and believing that exercise was the key to getting fit again. The weight loss wasn't intentional, but I didn't mind being a size 10.

Gradually, I became aware that none of my clothes fitted and my colleagues commented on my size. In total, I had lost 12 kg, approximately 20% of my body weight, over a period of 18 months, and had a BMI (body mass index) of less than 18. This meant I was underweight for my height. My clothes were now size six. I was borrowing trousers from Emily, my slight-in-frame 13-year-old daughter. It wasn't just the weight loss – there was a noticeable loss of muscle. There were gutters where I used to have muscles and I had to put a cushion on any hard chairs, otherwise sitting on them was too uncomfortable.

I thought the weight loss was mainly due to eating less. I was tending to eat a main meal at lunchtime and I omitted food in the evening after about 4 o'clock. Thankfully, following this regimen meant I had no further episodes of obstruction, fewer episodes of aspiration and I didn't require any courses of antibiotics. This had to be a good thing; Matthew was always berating me for taking them. I distinctly remember the smell of ketones, like pear drops or nail varnish remover, in my urine each morning. Subsequently, I realised this was due to muscle breakdown.

Although troublesome, the weight loss, abdominal pains and repeated chest infections didn't interfere with my ability to work. I put up with the fasciculations (muscle twitches) and fatigue. It was only once I developed joint pains that I really began to struggle and I was referred to a rheumatologist.

These pains occurred daily. Initially, they were in the balls of my feet and they responded to anti-inflammatory medicines and rest. I particularly noticed them in the mornings, when I put my feet on the floor. It was as though I was treading on shards of glass. I even checked the underside of my slippers to make sure there were no splinters. The pains were worse the day after I had exerted myself, but were most noticeable on waking. Then they spread to my wrists and ankles, such that it was painful to grip anything, for example a pen, or use a handbrake, or pick up a mug. Any attempt to hold or lift something would cause an excruciating, sharp pain to dart through my joints. I wondered if it was early rheumatoid arthritis, which runs in my family, but it was odd that I didn't have any swelling or real tenderness. In fact, when I squeezed my joints to see if they were tender it was the hand doing the squeezing that hurt, which made no sense.

Whilst awaiting the results of tests, I was given a high-dose steroid to see if it would help. The injection made me 'high', but then I started to shake and had difficulty walking. There were no erosions in the joints of my hands and feet. The condition was labelled non-destructive, non-specific arthropathy. The great news was that the blood tests showed I didn't have, and was unlikely to get, rheumatoid arthritis.

I was being listened to, but I wasn't getting any answers. I didn't know what was causing my symptoms and neither did anyone else. I was told it could be a seronegative arthritis – joint pains with normal blood tests and no erosions. I had a constellation of inexplicable symptoms and no obvious cause. I started treatment with hydroxychloroquine, which has a multitude of actions, none of them well understood. The drug is used as an anti-inflammatory; it's cheap and generally well tolerated, but I wasn't convinced it would do any good.

I felt frustrated with the system, and frequently wanted to give up. There were so many unexplained symptoms and it was becoming difficult to work out if they were real. I didn't want to look a fool in front of my colleagues, presenting as a malingerer, a fraud. It was almost as though I had to work out what was wrong with me before seeing anyone. I had been let down so many times before that except for a few trusted individuals, I had lost faith in the medical profession.

I also had problems with pruritis (itchy skin). My skin felt bumpy and irregular, and I had recurrent pus filled blisters. There were other infections, too: impetigo, ear infections, sinusitis and gingivitis. I didn't see a GP about the weight loss, but I did complain about the recurrent infections, thinking that maybe I had a problem with my immune system. I hadn't seen this particular doctor before and he remarked on my weight loss, commenting that he had to use the paediatric stethoscope. I was so thin that my ribs protruded through my skin. Neither of us knew what was wrong, but it was clear that I was sick. He referred me to a respiratory physician to investigate the recurrent chest infections.

A CT scan confirmed the aberrant right subclavian artery and congenital malrotation of my intestines. Unfortunately, no cause for the joint pains was found. I was disappointed, as I had already worked out that I had the two congenital abnormalities. The answer I was actually seeking was why did I have excruciating, crippling pains in my wrists, feet and ankles, and why was I getting so many infections? I'd already decided that I didn't want surgery for the other abnormalities and these symptoms were clearly not linked. Or were they? It seemed most unlikely.

Tangles

'MUM, DID YOU SAY THE DEADLINE for getting the washing done for the trip was tomorrow?' Emily asked, as she sauntered into our bedroom.

'Yes! If I am to wash, dry, iron, sort and have them ready I need your dirty clothes by tomorrow,' I replied. I was on a roll now, giving clear instructions to make absolutely sure Emily wasn't going to leave everything to the last minute, which was her usual fashion.

I continued to emphasise the point. 'So after tomorrow you can't wear any clothes . . .'

There was an embarrassing pause. Emily's eyebrows raised and then we both laughed. I'd intended to add, 'that you want to wear on the trip', but had stopped mid-sentence. One minute my speech was flowing smoothly, the next I lost my train of thought. The blanks were happening with alarming regularity. At least this time I was able to see the funny side and chuckled about my faux pas. Usually, I would get angry and feel full of rage and frustration. Emily swung out of the room clearly bemused, her hair arranged casually in a high ponytail, which she flicked as she returned to practise Beethoven's *Moonlight Sonata*.

I experienced the kind of woolly brain that pregnant women get, and I had a tendency to forget things or I struggled to concentrate. In my case, though, it was getting slightly worse every day, and I wasn't even expecting. I made light of it, reasoning that it was related to trying to juggle too many things. It wasn't until the meeting in London that I realised there was a problem, but even then I tried to tell myself I was being silly.

I was just tired. I obviously hadn't read the minutes, otherwise of course I would have remembered doing it. I tried to persuade myself that the fact I couldn't remember the process of reading them meant I hadn't read them. Although I still wasn't sure. I told myself that everyone has blanks. It's common practice to walk into a room to do something and forget what it is you are about to do. I carried on, but I became less and less convinced by my own excuses. Whenever I had forgotten why I was entering a room in the past, I had simply retraced my steps until it became clear. I would then remember the task and continue, slightly flustered, but back on target. Now these blanks were occurring at an alarming rate, and even retracing my steps failed to jog my memory – it just meant I walked further, with no positive outcome.

Then things started going missing in the house. The present and card for the children's birthday party; the form for the school trip that I had to complete, sign and hand back; the sewing kit I needed in order to sew the blazer buttons back on. It was usually things I knew I would need and so had put in a 'safe place'.

'Oh, Mum!' the children complained, exasperated with me, as I tried to pretend it was all part of a cunning plan and that I was totally in control.

'It'll turn up!' I would smile weakly, baffled by my own stupidity.

'But I have to hand it in today, otherwise I can't go on the trip,' Tom announced.

'It's all right, I'll write a letter instead.'

'Okaaay!' he sighed, indicating it clearly wasn't OK. 'It's not in a safe place, is it?' he half joked. A 'safe place' had become a euphemism for 'Mummy's lost it!'

There was usually a way around such problems, but what worried me was that I had no recollection of putting the offending items in their safe place. I had no memory of my actions.

I became obsessive about my belongings and kept anything important next to my side of the bed. I had systems in place so that it would be easy to locate things and I became a stickler for tidiness, although, in truth, the house was becoming increasingly disorganised. The frustration was awful, so I had multiple outbursts of anger, usually when I felt out of control and often about ridiculously insignificant issues. I would suddenly shout and sound ferociously cross, before becoming extremely shaky and feeling embarrassed, as the situation didn't really necessitate that kind of overreaction. I was unable to restrain my emotions. It was as though the mechanism for dampening this fevered eruption had ceased to function.

As I deteriorated I became reluctant to start a conversation, as I worried I would forget what I was trying to say mid-sentence. I had difficulty recalling names or words, which made me even more cross and upset. I became emotionally labile and was unable to control periods of inappropriate tearfulness, as well as the angry outbursts. I was regressing, but instead of returning to the typical toddler picture of sunshine and showers, my forecast was thunder and foggy patches. Even the lightening-sharp pains in my joints had dulled.

Do I have early dementia? I questioned, scared that I was developing neurofibrillary tangles in my brain to match the frizzy, dry hair on my head. I thought of my brain being smothered by beta-amyloid plaques – one of the abnormal proteins formed in the brain in Alzheimer's dementia – like a fleece over the winter vegetables in the garden, or a blanket of snow dumbing noise and numbing senses. The colours had been washed out of my life.

Crab Apples

I STILL HAD CLEAR MEMORIES OF OUR family holidays. Speeding or ambling, heading straight or turning sharply. One minute you are cruising in the fast lane in an air-conditioned car, the wind slipping past, exhilarated and enjoying the freedom, unaware or simply oblivious to any admirers or coveters, the next you are backing the MPV out of a multistorey car park on a busy Saturday in Durham city, having forgotten that the roof box exceeds the height restriction.

It was 2003, the first day of the school holidays, and we were the centre of attention, trying to ignore the glances and the obvious frustration (or was it entertainment?) on people's faces. If only the concrete slope would sink like the sensation in the pit of my stomach, and swallow us up through the teeth-lined opening to the car park.

The destination this time was Northumberland for a week of castles, gardens, windswept rocky coastline and Craster kippers. We had to make frequent stops on our journey, and I'd watch the children play, hoping they would sleep in the car for the rest of the drive. It occurred to me, not for the first time, how much effort it took to keep on top of things. Becoming a doctor, being married, having four children – I had wanted it all (career and family) – and I took my health for granted. Why shouldn't I? After all, I looked after myself. I allowed myself a moment of self-satisfied pride.

One of the stops en route to the holiday in Northumberland was at Woolsthorpe Manor in Lincolnshire. After a brief run around the farm buildings and the museum, it was clear the girls weren't interested in the immaculately presented displays, but I wanted to show them why this was on our list of places to visit.

'Emily! Anna! Come over here! Come on, stand under the tree!' I called out to them.

My two beautiful daughters scampered over.

'Now, look over there,' I said, pointing at the farm building. The girls obediently looked over, expecting to see something exciting. Standing behind them, in the long wet grass at the base of the tree, I dropped a small apple on each of their heads. Their reactions were instant and they looked up at me with cheeky grins. They could see the fun but not the point.

'Ow! Muuum! Why?' Anna said, rubbing her head, pretending to be hurt. She could be comical in familiar company, but was excruciatingly shy with strangers.

'What's that for?' Emily boldly joined in the protest.

We all giggled at their surprise. I was enjoying the game of getting them interested in the science, but keeping their attention long enough to stop them running off to kick piles of leaves at their little brother was hard.

'The man who used to live here was called Isaac Newton,' I began to explain. 'He was a brilliant scientist and the first to work out why we stay on the ground and why those apples fell on your heads. An apple fell on his head, too, just here. Maybe that's what made him think about it, but he was probably clever enough to reach his conclusion without having to have an apple bump him on the head. And the reason he worked it out was because he asked himself a really good question. He asked "why?"'

The girls looked as though this had made an impression. I wondered if they would be great scientists one day. Meanwhile, two-year-old Tom charged over, snot dribbling out of both barrels. He tried to throw apples at his sisters and put all his effort into a throw that left a bruised, red crab apple resting by his feet. He looked at it for a moment, seemingly unsure of how it got there, before picking it up again and toddling after his older siblings. Emily and Anna ran off screaming and laughing.

'Mum! Make him stop!' Anna protested. Tom chuckled. He thought Anna was egging him on and started to pick up more apples.

Tom and Anna were always fighting. It was one of the reasons we had decided to have four children, so that Anna wouldn't be the middle child. I often joked that we now had two middle children.

We were back in the car again, returning from the smokehouse at Craster, where we were able to show the children the curing process and pick up a couple of amber-coloured kippers for breakfast.

'Matthew!' I shrieked.

I ducked, only realising afterwards that it wouldn't help. The railway bridge was extremely low and the MPV, with the roof box on top, only just cleared the bridge.

The holiday in Northumberland was great fun. Emily ran wild along the cliff tops and was thrilled by the stormy sea and her first experience of rock pooling. Anna loved visiting Harry Potter's castle in Alnwick. We invented a new game called 'Where's Tommy?' I was holding onto each girl and carrying baby Edward in a papoose. Meanwhile, Matthew struggled with Tom, who regularly escaped from his grasp and disappeared into the crowd. Tom thought this was hugely funny.

'Where's Tommy?' I berated Matthew, when I realised our boy was missing. Acknowledging that Matthew actually had the more difficult job in holding on to him, I resisted the temptation to remind him that he only had *one* child to keep under control. Tom was eventually found. He was in the Poisons Garden. Luckily, he was far more interested in the new game than sampling any of the plants.

Somehow Tommy had survived. I smiled to myself, remembering some difficult periods, but also some very happy times.

Second Chance

IT HADN'T BEEN EASY COMBINING medical training with a family, just as it hadn't been easy applying for medicine in the first place. I remembered the careers advice: out of the nine pupils in my school year hoping to be doctors, seven were girls. The advice from my teacher was to become a radiographer, like his daughter had, and to simply marry a doctor (he seemed to think this a good compromise). It was meant kindly, but the underlying message received was: 'Why worry our pretty heads trying to achieve when we could marry into a proxy status?'

After the children were born, I continued to work full-time, and organising a changing crew of nannies and home helps was part of the challenge. I managed by being ultra organised. At work, I knew I was operating in a man's world and even adopted the 'besuited' look: tailored jacket, trousers, shirt, cufflinks and flats.

*

I met Matthew in 1995, while I was in Cambridge doing my postgraduate training in gastroenterology. I had been called to a cardiac arrest and hurried to a ward side room to find two nurses resuscitating the patient – one was doing chest compressions while the other tried to give the patient oxygen. Checking for a pulse, I looked at the ECG monitor – it showed PEA (pulseless electrical activity) – the heart rhythm was continuing but there was no effective pulse. In other words, the wiring was intact but the pump had failed. I quickly thought through the reversible causes – the four H's and four T's – hypovolaemia (low blood volume usually due to blood loss), hyperkalaemia (high potassium), hypothermia, hypoxia (lack of oxygen), tension pneumothorax (a collapsed lung under pressure), thromboembolism (a massive blood clot), tamponade (fluid in the space around the heart, preventing the heart from beating) and finally, toxins (drugs and poisons).

'OK, well done, Amy,' I said. 'Can you carry on doing chest compressions?'

I had learnt the value of using colleagues' names in emergency situations. It wasn't always easy; there were often unfamiliar faces. New nurses started all the time, as there was a high turnover in this department, or the ones in were doing supply shifts to make up for all the vacancies. It was much better to work with a team I knew. Thinking of the next steps, I looked for the adrenaline syringe on the emergency trolley and started the stopwatch.

All the doctors were trained in life-support techniques, practising drills on mannequins to ensure skills were slick. The training courses were designed to make the actual cardiac arrests less stressful, however, the courses were tense; if you kept to the protocol the mannequin lived, but failing under the eyes of peers was dreaded – it made the interminable 48-hour duties seem routine.

Cardiac arrests like this happened every day on call. I assumed my role as team captain and gave instructions to the rest of the group, which now included the nursing staff on the unit and junior doctors. Looking up, I saw I was being watched. The anaesthetist at the head end of the patient had swiftly sorted out the airway and, with a flick of his hair, had an endotracheal tube connected and was calmly ventilating the patient after each cycle of chest compressions, whilst continuing to observe me.

Reviewing the patient's chart, I could see that he had been deteriorating all day. The nurses had charted the blood pressure, pulse and respiratory rate, and even though the blood pressure had remained adequate, the pulse rate and respiratory rate were high, and had been getting higher.

'What access do we have? We need to give a bolus of fluid,' I instructed the team, efficiently managing the situation.

The anaesthetist grinned. He was tanned, with smiling eyes, a thick mane of sun-bleached hair and a confident manner. I hadn't seen him before and assumed he must have just started. I was now in my fourth year as a doctor, having moved from Southampton to Cambridge via Oxford. I had previously worked with liver specialists and, inspired by their research and clinical skills, had decided to train to be a specialist in liver disease.

Slowly, the patient responded to fluid resuscitation, and when Amy stopped the cardiac compressions I could feel a faint pulse. He was relatively young, with alcoholic liver disease, and this was his first presentation to hospital. I could see that he had a large abdominal girth, which shook with each cardiac compression. This was due to a significant volume of ascites (fluid in his abdomen). Thinking of the possible causes of his deterioration, I thought it likely he had spontaneous bacterial peritonitis (infection in this fluid), although it was possible that he also had a concurrent chest infection, as he wasn't able to expand his chest because of all the fluid below his diaphragm. He was jaundiced and had florid spider naevi on his skin (the red spots due to damaged tiny blood vessels seen in chronic alcoholics).

With more intravenous fluid, his pulse strengthened and his blood pressure became measurable. He had pulled through. My thoughts turned to what to do next. He was clearly very sick and would die without close monitoring and treatment in intensive care. Even with prolonged supportive treatment his outlook was poor. Unlike kidney failure, for which dialysis is life saving, there was no machine to do the work of the failed liver in these patients, leaving death all too often inevitable. Perhaps he could be improved and then he may be suitable for liver transplantation, but he would need to be stable first. Besides, with infection, malnutrition and immunosuppression, I knew he was a poor candidate for a transplant. There was also a chronic shortage of organs. Despite all this I felt we had to give him a second chance.

The anaesthetist talked to the intensive care doctor on the phone, painting a bleak but honest picture of the man, with the likelihood that he would not survive. He was pushing for a ceiling of care on the ward – he thought the patient should stay put. In my mind this meant certain death. I thought this was unfair and I was willing the patient to live. Ignoring my emotions and thinking practically, the patient had already proven that ward care was insufficient for his needs. Also, the nurses on the ward wouldn't be able to manage treating him – there were simply too many patients for each nurse to care for, which was part of the reason he had deteriorated to this state in the first place. But I was struck by the anaesthetist's honesty – he was being realistic. In spite of his concerns, the patient was admitted to Intensive Care. Unfortunately, as predicted, after weeks on the unit, he died.

A few weeks later, Heather, my fellow gastroenterology trainee, invited me on a punting trip in Cambridge. I cycled from home into the city, past the Botanical Gardens, up

Trumpington Road and onto the Fen Causeway – countryside in the centre of the city. A swan sat quietly on her nest, which was made from a haphazard pile of sticks, and nettles and bushes grew untended; it was shabby, unkempt and natural, a world away from the fumes belched out by buses and cars nearby. Livestock has been kept on the meadows for centuries, and the Fen was crisscrossed with paths over which cows roamed, unperturbed by the scatty doctor wearing a peach and yellow floral dress, with tangles of frizzy hair escaping her cycling helmet. I met Heather by the bridge, by which time I was flushed and out of breath. I'd left work late and pedalled frantically to get there on time. On the grass by the river, groups of students, locals and tourists sat out in the late summer sunshine. Parents marshalled children drawn to the noise and foaming water at the weir. Under the willow tree, talking with the others and partially hidden by the hanging lime-yellow leaves, was the anaesthetist I had met at the cardiac arrest. Heather introduced me to Matthew.

★

My friend Heather had seemed so sensible. She obviously wasn't entirely level-headed, though, when you considered her choice of housemates. Heather had trained in London, but through friends was renting a shared house with a number of male doctors, all of whom had trained in Birmingham. Matthew had also trained in the city and was pals with Heather's housemates. They were known collectively as 'Scum from Brum', and Heather would regale me with great tales of the skullduggery and mischievousness in the house. These were mostly relayed with a mock sense of disgust, whilst in fact she generally found their antics amusing. There were late-night fry-ups and general mess making, but the worst incident occurred on a house ski trip. One night, the boys drank far too much, leaving the sink full of dirty water, floating fat scum and broken glasses. They hit the slopes the following morning after breakfast, leaving the mess for the poor chalet girl to clear up. But they got their comeuppance. They were so hungover that the swaying of the ski lift was too much and one of them vomited off the lift and onto the piste below.

Heather enjoyed a sense of superiority over her housemates' domestic incompetence, but then Taf (they all had made up names from their student rugby tour days; the meanings, if explained, made no sense unless you had been there in the same inebriated state to appreciate the humour) put her Clinique soap in the washing machine to clean his cycling Lycra. He was rather pleased with the effect on his padded shorts. Heather was horrified and it was almost the end of domestic harmony.

★

One night, I stayed over with Heather and was awoken by the sensation of being watched. Standing over my bed were two tall strangers, whose wiry physiques and masses of wild curly hair filled me with terror. This was worse than faces at the window – a longstanding, irrational fear of mine. My assailants were actually in my bedroom. I shrieked, suddenly fully alert and filled with a sense of panic, my heart pounding. With only the dim light from the landing silhouetting their bodies, and in the unfamiliar surroundings, I could not recognise them. I thought I was about to be raped or murdered in my bed . . .

Taf and his best friend Cub were always playing pranks. One such trick involved dressing up in curly wigs and sneaking into other people's bedrooms in the early hours of the morning after a late drinking session. They were both a bit sheepish the next morning, apologising reluctantly at Heather's insistence.

Sick Chicks and Ducklings

2007

'WHAT DO YOU THINK YOU'RE DOING, you don't belong in here?' I said to Chippers sternly, whilst trying to shoo her out of the kitchen.

Chippers looked at me, head tilted to one side, and as though taking it all in, she turned around, lifted her tail and deposited a gift on the kitchen floor before strutting out again. She was the children's favourite hen. However, she also lacked a sense of space and overdid the free-range thing. The front door of our converted barn was always open and Chippers had no doubt followed one of the children inside.

'Ew! 'uk! Dat Tippers?' Edward chuckled mischievously. Boys are always tickled by bodily functions. He had wandered into the kitchen to find me clearing up the chicken poo. Edward, freckly and smiling, was always happy and found everything amusing. He had short, sandy hair in tight curls. It took four children to get one with my curly hair! Matthew and I both agreed that we couldn't imagine our family without Edward; it was now complete. When he was born, however, Anna hadn't been so sure. 'I don't want another b'other, I want a sister called Mary,' she had stated.

On the other hand, Tom had been delighted, grabbing his baby brother around the neck and chanting: 'Mine!'

The house was surrounded by acres of land. There were plenty of trees to climb, ditches for building dens and an enormous greenhouse attached to a spacious black barn. The barn contained machinery and large motors; there were metal shelves full of nuts and bolts, irrigation pipes, and reels of heavy-duty copper wire. The greenhouse was industrial sized, an acre in area and higher than a double decker bus. It was great for drying wood and washing, and it had amazing acoustics. Otherwise, though, it was an eyesore. The children bragged that you could even see it from space (it was obvious on Google Earth at least). At a dinner party one evening, I discussed the subject of wood burners with someone visiting the country from London. They boasted that they had kiln-dried wood delivered to their door. I smiled – I had 'greenhouse dried' wood delivered by wheelbarrow, if I could persuade one of the children to fetch it for me!

'But there was a rat in the greenhouse,' Emily complained when asked to do wood duty.

'It was horrid. Nasty beady eyes,' Anna joined in, a concerned expression on her face; her wavy, blonde locks bobbing as she cocked her head to one side, her innocent blue eyes wide open beneath fluttering eyelashes. It was a look of determination – there was no way she was going to go anywhere near the allegedly rat-infested woodpile.

At least the house was dry, and although it was rather small we had plenty of storage space in the old barns. The L-shaped barn with a pantile roof was falling down; it had wattle and daub walls and wood-wormed beams and partitions. The black barn had space for bikes, trailers, toys and boxes of gear that wouldn't yet fit into the house. The only real problem we had was the sewage pit, which probably dated from the Victorian era, and the sewage pipes, which seemed to run uphill around the back of the house. For whatever reason there was a frequent problem with backup. The system probably hadn't been designed to cope with this number of residents. The other problem was that the house was on a slope and the runoff from the land collected in the backyard, creating a flash flood every time there was heavy rainfall. It was ironic, as to avoid suffering from flood damage we had purposely not bought a house in the valley or on a flood plain. However, it was nothing that a new sewage tank and drainage couldn't fix – these just needed to be added to the long list of jobs still to be done. More urgently, the pond had to be fenced off and all the disgusting carpets removed from the house. Planting an orchard also made it onto this pressing list. It gave us a tremendous feeling of hope and happiness when we chose the trees at the nursery: Adam's Pearmain – or 'Norfolk Pippin' – an old English desert apple, Horsford Prolific – a large, sweet, red and yellow-skinned apple, Cox, Egremont Russell and Bramley. The apple trees were each planted in a bed of compost. The orchard was arranged in formation and using stakes and wire, the trees were protected from the ravages of the wind, deer, and small boys with footballs.

Over the years we had lots of chickens, and at one stage there were three cockerels. The children named them Cock, Doodle and Boo. Watching the chickens, I noticed the cockerels strutting around the garden in their self-important manner, the hens following. If they didn't peck in the right places, the cockerels would have little tantrums, stomping their claws on the ground. It was not dissimilar to some of my less enlightened colleagues in the hospital.

Each cockerel had its own clutch of hens. As hens are fickle, this number varied. Cock and Doodle both picked on Boo, whom Anna had renamed Billy. One night, Billy disappeared and never returned. Cock and Doodle then fought with each other; pecking furiously, spurs ripping at each other's necks, bright red blood spattering, feathers flying and becoming matted in dark, congealed blood. I had seen plenty of sights in the hospital, but still the animal instinct to maim or kill was frightening.

Despite the cockfights, the country was a great place for us to live. Matthew had a safe route off the beaten track to cycle to work, and I saw the changing seasons in the farming year as I drove along the country roads. We were next to a wooded valley and surrounded by fields and copses. The children had the freedom to run wild and get filthy, as well as learning about looking after animals and dealing with death. In addition to the chickens we kept rare-breed sheep. We were immersed in nature: there were partridges, pheasants, ducks, owls, deer, hares, foxes, rabbits, hedgehogs, mice and moles.

We were involved in several successful rescue efforts, such as the baby rabbit that kept coming into the house through the cat flap. I had no idea how soft rabbit fur was or how one small creature could be capable of making so many droppings. As I grabbed hold of it to put it outside, I learnt that rabbits make an absolutely terrifying shriek when caught, a noise you could often hear at night when the barn owl was hunting. Other more daring rescue attempts included a very cold hedgehog that we fished out of the swimming pool one November. (Matthew was keen to fill in the swimming pool, which had been put in by previous owners and was a deep, green oblong mass of water surrounded by concrete paving slabs, but every summer for a few weeks it was the source of fun and laughter.) The hedgehog was caught in a net and gently warmed (though almost cooked) on the AGA.

Another time we rescued a neighbour's obese Labrador from the pool. It had howled all night, but I wrongly assumed the cry was a fox's mating call. It wasn't until I went into

Anna's room to wake her for school, and heard the howling followed by splashing, that I looked out of the window and realised what had happened. The poor animal was exhausted and it would have been unlikely to survive much longer.

'Dog! Swimming pool! Everyone up! Now!' I shouted.

Wearing only my dressing gown, I ran to the side of the pool and somehow managed to heave the dopey, stinky creature out of the water. The grateful animal immediately shook his bedraggled coat and sprayed me with foul-smelling water. That morning, it was more difficult than usual to get everyone up, cleaned, dressed, breakfasted and into school and work on time. Despite marks for originality, the children's excuses did not sound convincing to their teachers.

The tame hen, Chippers, was one of the first chicks to survive despite a strange weakness – there had been a few before her that had been left to nature and sadly died. From each clutch, a few of the chicks lost the ability to walk. Within the first few days of hatching they became unstable and then too weak to perch on their feet, sitting back and resting on the ground. Finally, they would fall over, lifting up their heads as though looking up at the stars, their beaks opening and closing as death became imminent.

When Chippers became too weak to stand, we brought her into the kitchen in a shoebox, where she was regularly fed with a liquid chick feed using a pipette. She slowly recovered, initially able to perch, then to make a few steps, until it became impossible to keep her in a box. She was transferred to an indoor crate, from which she would regularly escape. Perhaps she had overstayed her welcome, preferring the engaging company of the children. She would follow them around whenever she saw them, attempting to become one of the family.

A peculiar ailment was clearly affecting the yellow, fluffy chicks and after the first few cases, I decided to do some research online and consulted our trusty handbook, which Matthew jokingly referred to as *The Chicken Bible.* I decided that it must have been a type of encephalitis virus. Bird flu was rife at the time and whilst keeping sick chicks inside wasn't smart or clever, we weren't in the affected zone so it wasn't against the law. Also, this wasn't really the same as bird flu, and it only affected newborn chicks and never more than three in each clutch. I brushed aside my concerns and decided not to alert the authorities. When the problem began to recur again and again, the encephalitis virus seemed an unlikely explanation, but it wasn't bird flu either.

Strangely, there had been a similar disease affecting the pale yellow and grey mottled ducklings in the enclosed garden of the house we had rented in Haarlem, Holland, a few years earlier, before Tom was born. We were there for eight months whilst Matthew completed a fellowship prior to applying for a consultant post. One by one these ducklings developed what seemed to be a neurological condition: a weakness characterised by difficulty walking and then perching when it seemed they could no longer use their legs. Finally, they fell onto their sides, their necks arched. It was so sad to watch. Over a few weeks each duckling succumbed to the fatal, mystery illness.

*

As I closed the chickens away in the dark, I saw beady red eyes flickering like devils in the blackness. Standing still, I heard ghostlike scuffling. I started to move again and was sure I had almost trodden on one. Apparently, for every rat spotted there will be another 20, so for every rat I had almost trampled there were probably another hundred. In short, we had a big rodent problem. I told Matthew and we both agreed something had to be done. He promised to deal with the situation the next time he had a free weekend.

Rats are cunning, and, unfortunately, they are inevitable around chickens. Poisoning them was going to be tricky. Most rat poisons work by blocking vitamin K. The chickens were fed corn and there was also sweetcorn growing in the adjacent vegetable plot. The corn provided the rats with the natural antidote, plenty of vitamin K, to cure them of the effects of the poison. Rats also need water and as the vegetable plot had been dug next to the pond, they had the ideal conditions for breeding.

'Edward, what are you doing?' I asked my six-year-old son in a manner that sounded as though I was reprimanding him. 'What do you need those matches for?'

'Dad asked me to get them,' he replied, as he ran out of the kitchen.

That Saturday was a pleasant autumn day; dry with little wind and ideal for a bonfire. I thought I better follow and set off past the orchard, up the slight incline to the back of the black barn and the bonfire site. All was quiet in the top field; there was no evidence of father or son. As I walked back down the slope towards the house, I could see them over by the pond. Edward was standing on top of the compost heap.

'What are you doing?' I asked, slightly exasperated. I seemed to spend a lot of time these days trying to keep some semblance of order and normality in our lives.

'Rats! Dad's going to fix the rats,' Edward explained, as though it should be obvious.

Father and son were busy with rags and a bottle. The plan was to smoke the vermin out. Matthew had started digging in the compost heap and had worked out it was home to many rodents. There were multiple rat holes in the heap; hence this plot would solve the rat problem. It was not dissimilar to one of the methods the mole man used; when he wasn't setting traps he put chemicals in the mole passages.

I returned to the house, leaving the boys to their cunning scheme. Shortly afterwards I heard shrieks of laughter. Edward came running into the house, chuckling and breathless, his whole body jiggling with mirth. He was barely able to mutter the syllables. 'Kaboom! Kaboom!'

Matthew followed, and he was also laughing so much he could barely speak. Tears streamed from his eyes, or at least I assumed they were tears, rather than irritation from smoke and fumes.

'It was so funny.'

They were both talking excitedly at the same time, waving their hands in the air to relive the effect.

'Kaboom!'

'It exploded the compost heap.'

'The compost heap! Kaboom!'

'Kaboom!'

'Smoky.'

'And Edward's face.'

After the giggles had subsided and they had both calmed down, I was given the full story. Matthew had come up with a brilliant idea. He had intended to smoke the rats out of the compost heap and possibly even suffocate them to death in it.

Whilst digging, he had realised that the rat tunnels went deep into the heap. He'd decided that stuffing rags soaked in petrol into each of the holes and then lighting them would have the desired effect – a rat-free property. Edward stood on top of the heap, holding a spade and keeping a keen eye out for any rats trying to escape. This was in case an amendment to the plan was required (I didn't enquire what this might be). The first rag was lit with a match and suddenly 'Kaboom', the whole compost heap exploded, with Edward lifted a few centimetres into the air. (In time with retelling, this has become a few feet.)

They found out by accident that all the rat tunnels in the compost heap were connected. Interestingly, the rodents were using the underground irrigation pipe to the greenhouse as a rat run. This explained why there were so many rats on the woodpile. Rats are incontinent, dribbling urine as they scurry, and, as rat urine carries disease, Anna had been right in her reluctance to collect wood. It certainly made more sense. There was no source of food or water in the greenhouse, so I wondered what the attraction was. The compost heap produced a combustible gas. By lighting one rag, Matthew had blown up the whole heap. Luckily, there was no back explosion into the greenhouse, and no one, except a few hundred rats, was hurt. The rat population was considerably reduced.

★

One morning, a few weeks later, Matthew and I were having breakfast in the kitchen whilst watching a deer graze in the garden. It was eating the newly planted laurel hedge around the swimming pool and was seemingly unbothered by human presence in such close proximity; admittedly, the boys were still asleep. Once the whole household was awake, it quickly disappeared. We went out for the day and when we returned later we found the deer floating in the swimming pool; unfortunately, it had become trapped between the pool steps and the side of the pool. Although dead, it was still warm, which meant it must have died very recently.

'What are you doing?' I asked Matthew, acutely aware that I was using the same tone that I used to speak to the children and even the naughty hen, Chippers. He was dragging the dead deer up to the large barn.

'These will make great beating sticks,' he replied, as if it required no explanation. Amongst the broken mowers, old bicycles and garden furniture, the deer's small antlers were sawn off to use as decorative tops on wooden sticks for Edward and Tom to use when helping with the beating at shoots – Matthew and the boys enthusiastically engaged in all the countryside sports on offer. Matthew was suspiciously quiet and out of sight for several hours, and then the deer's hind leg made it into the AGA. Intuitively, I knew that the rest would have been packed into one of the freezers, but I wasn't keen to broach the subject just then; I would secretly dispose of the other three limbs in due course. The meat was extremely tough and understandably the children refused to eat it.

Adding Salt to Crisps

WHEN I WAS A HOUSE OFFICER, the most junior member of the team, the daily ward rounds were conducted in the traditional way: all equipped with white coats, the senior registrar, registrar, two senior house officers, two house officers, and usually a medical student on a 10-week placement, would review the patients. Twice a week the consultant would conduct the ward round and the registrar would present each patient. I would listen to the history and the examination findings, as recorded on admission by one of the juniors. The results of any blood tests would be reviewed and then we would all walk over to the X-ray box and view any films of the patient.

At that time, it was quite difficult to see anything useful on a CT, since the images were so small, without the means of enlarging them, as, thanks to modern digital technology, we can now do. However, there were benefits to the old system. The doctor who had seen the patient was able to interpret the film. Now the X-ray specialist stays in a dark room remote from the sick person. The processes have adapted with technological advances, but these have introduced new problems.

On ward rounds, the consultant leading our team would pose questions to certain members, which were relevant to the patient in front of them.

'What are the causes of hypercalcaemia?' (High calcium levels.)

'Hyperparathyroidism, malignancy, excess vitamin D, renal failure,' would be a reasonable response.

'And in this man with back pain and high globulins?'

The consultant would then grill the house officer about abnormally high levels of these proteins found in the blood.

'I would want to exclude multiple myeloma but also consider malignancy such as primary lung or prostate,' would be one correct reply.

I remember my registrar teaching me that bone metastasis were 'all the Bs'. He had laughed as he said, 'Bronchus, breast, bidney, byroid, brostate!'

It was a helpful way to remember which cancers spread to bone.

Back when I was a medical student, a consultant asked me during clinic to list the causes of peripheral neuropathy (nerve damage). I really struggled and so the consultant gave me a pneumonic to help me remember: Vitamin deficiencies (B vitamins mostly), Infections (leprosy), Toxins (drugs and alcohol), Amyloid, Metabolic (including diabetes), Inflammation and Neoplasm (cancer). It spelt VITAMIN. I later added C to remind myself that connective tissue disorders could also cause peripheral neuropathy.

As students, we learnt to think in patterns and to recognise the common disease associations and presentations. The patients we saw left an imprint, like a short code, to be retrieved from the file at a later date when certain symptoms were encountered again. We also learnt from instances when the information presented did not tally with one of these diseases.

The importance of ascertaining the symptoms was emphasised, as was the saying: 'Eighty per cent of the diagnosis is in the history.' I was also taught that if the diagnosis wasn't initially clear, it was essential to retake the history, ask in more detail, or change the questions. Revisiting the history often made things clearer. Investigations were performed to confirm or refute the working diagnosis.

Increasingly, medicine is not being practised this way. Doctors tend to rely too heavily on blood tests and arrange further investigations based on the results of these, rather than the likelihood of the diagnosis based on clinical suspicion from the history. It is also easy to be falsely reassured by normal or negative tests, even though it is known that tests are not 100% reliable, sometimes not even 80% reliable. I have been fooled in this way.

2009

It was my Tuesday evening on call, or 'Mummy's long day', as Edward called it. I was asked to see a female patient on the unit who might be able to be discharged, as her blood tests were normal. Although the patient had been referred with a collapse, she now had a stable, normal blood pressure and was keen to go home.

As usual, there were insufficient beds for the emergency patients. The hospital always seemed to prioritise the elective surgical programme. This was a by-product of the fact that hospitals were now being run as businesses. Since the invention of surgical targets, there were seldom cancellations in surgery, but, paradoxically, the number of emergency admissions was more predictable. Elective surgery fluctuated wildly according to holidays and medical meetings. The beds available for emergencies seemed to depend on the time of year and the number of planned operations (the number of available consultant surgeons), rather than the number of beds needed to assess and treat sick patients in an appropriate manner. In order to try to reduce the burden of emergencies on hospitals, politicians devised a scheme whereby the amount of money paid to hospitals to see acutely unwell patients was drastically cut. Obviously, this would make patients much better and instantly reduce the need for patients to come to hospital! I was irked by this, but endeavoured to practise holistically and not be swayed by management issues. Even so, I had to adapt my way of working, and I was now seeing this patient in the 'treatment room', which was actually a poorly lit store cupboard with a trolley in it, surrounded by sterile packs and equipment. I did the assessment whilst the nurses interrupted repeatedly to pick up dressing packs.

The patient had been living and working abroad, but had returned to the UK due to ill health. Her nausea, vomiting and abdominal pain had been investigated, but the gastroenterologists had not found any abnormalities in her guts. She had never been overweight, and had lost weight whilst living abroad; at present, her weight was steady. I was struggling to explain her symptoms, particularly the collapse, so I asked her to come back to the hospital if her symptoms recurred.

Unbeknown to me, the patient returned to the Emergency Department (ED) a week later and was told by the doctors there that she had an eating disorder. Four weeks after this she was referred by her GP, who was also baffled by her symptoms, but clearly recognised that there was a problem. On this occasion, the patient had marked postural hypotension so that whenever she stood up she felt very dizzy, since her blood pressure fell precipitously. A fall in blood pressure of up to 20 mm Hg (blood pressure is recorded in millimetres of mercury, as the old sphygmomanometers measure blood pressure according to a mercury tube) is tolerated reasonably well, but hers was falling 50-60 mm Hg. At home she had felt so unwell that she had resorted to crawling to get around. In daylight I could now see that she was remarkably tanned. It was true that she had lived abroad, but it now transpired that it was a year since she had last been in a hot climate. As it was February and her tan was still present, this was clearly abnormal.

The diagnosis became clear, and I had missed it on our previous encounter: she had Addison's disease, usually due to an autoimmune condition of the adrenal gland, which, if she had developed an infection, would be life-threatening. Her cortisol was very low. I looked back at my notes to see why it had not occurred to me on the previous admission. I definitely hadn't noticed her tanned skin, as I recalled seeing her in the dimly lit store cupboard. Her blood pressure had been normal when I saw her lying down. Unusually for a patient with Addison's disease, she had completely normal electrolytes (sodium and potassium). Almost every patient I had seen or heard of, and it is an unusual condition, had low sodium or, more commonly, high potassium, or both electrolytes were outside the normal range. I had been falsely reassured by the normal blood test result. I felt bad for not thinking of Addison's in the first instance. I explained the diagnosis to the patient and admitted that I had relied too much on the investigations rather than what she had told me, which amounted to the classic symptoms of Addison's disease.

'Would adding salt to my food have anything to do with the normal sodium levels?' she asked.

'It might do,' I replied. I wasn't entirely sure if it would make the sodium and potassium levels entirely normal.

'I eat salt out of a pot,' she continued. 'I even add it to crisps. I've been doing it for years – my friends and family are so used to seeing me do it that it's normal for them.'

It turned out my patient was 'addicted' to salt, but not quite in the same way as alcoholics or drug addicts are addicted. Salt craving is a recognised symptom of Addison's disease, but I had never heard of a patient *treating* herself with it. I also reflected on the fact that I asked my patients many questions, but seldom enquired about their diet, yet it is so important. In this case, a history of a dietary quirk may have led to an earlier diagnosis, possibly even years earlier. A simple question about eating habits might have revealed all. I resorted to the journals, or rather the printed articles online, to investigate 'salt treatment'.

There was an article from 1936[2], which was the recordings of a round-table discussion, equivalent to a forum these days, I suppose. They reviewed the history of salt treatment and reported that animals with Addison's disease lived longer if they were given intravenous salt solution. A few years after this, salt was used for the first time to treat a patient with this condition. The patient felt better and the sodium measured in the blood normalised. The paper then described a small number of patients who had been treated with salt and who survived for a variable period before succumbing to the disease. For a while, advice to eat salt became a standard treatment of Addison's disease. Salt treatment had the added advantage that less cortisol extract was required. However, it was clear that large doses of salt were necessary in order for it to be effective.

There was another patient whom I recalled diagnosing with Addison's disease, but in her case she had abnormal electrolytes and dangerously low blood pressure. The biochemist had made a rare venture out of the lab to tell me that her cortisol level was so low it was virtually unrecordable. I was proud to have made the correct diagnosis, particularly as for many years the patient had also been identified as having an 'eating disorder'. I administered the life-saving cortisol hormone and some saline to correct the blood pressure and normalise the electrolytes. I was having a celebratory cup of tea in the office with the junior doctors, educating them on the diagnosis of Addison's, when the nurse burst into the office. The patient's blood pressure had fallen again and the fluid wasn't helping. She was critically unwell, and although Addison's is now a fully treatable condition, she was extremely sick, having presented so late.

The patient had to be transferred to Intensive Care for closer monitoring. She was haemodynamically unstable (low blood pressure), and possibly septic. As a consultant, I was continually learning. The first dose of cortisol had helped initially, but as all the patient's cells were starved of cortisol, the relatively small dose I'd administered had been like a drop in the ocean. In order to maintain her blood pressure, what she actually needed was cortisol infusion (continuous drip feed of the hormone). With the correct treatment she survived, but she may not have done had she presented much later.

It is now accepted that if a patient with diabetes becomes unwell they will require additional insulin over the course of the illness. At the time of this round-table discussion, the experts didn't know this, but they correctly predicted that it would be the same for cortisol deficiency.

This is often the time when patients present in an 'Addison's crisis'; an intercurrent illness requires additional cortisol and the body deteriorates into stress mode, unable to support an adequate blood pressure. These clever doctors suggested that in this situation it would make sense to give larger amounts of cortisol and intravenous saline. Their common-sense approach proved to be correct.

Sadly, the paper also highlighted the fact that treatment with cortisol was expensive, and in the pre-National Health Service era, most patients simply could not afford to take the extract, or sufficient amounts of the extract, so they had to supplement their diet with salt, often inadequately, which meant that sooner or later they would die of the disease. The demise in each of these cases seemed to be precipitated by an acute illness.

In 1855, Thomas Addison, a British physician and dermatologist, described the characteristic findings in 11 patients with a bronze skin condition that caused discolouration of the entire body surface. He not only described his patients, he also performed autopsies, enabling him to discover the underlying pathology. Addison is considered the founder of the speciality of medicine called endocrinology.[3] The descriptions of his patients were recorded decades before the cause was actually identified. Addison's disease was known as the great mimicker, like syphilis. Cortisol deficiency is very diverse in its presentation; the symptoms vary widely between individuals. It is therefore tricky to diagnose.

I reflected on why I had not made the diagnosis of Addison's disease in the patient with normal electrolytes. My short-code retrieval system had failed – it had been overridden by the normal electrolytes. I had been misled by the normal results, but it wasn't just that. The patient had inadvertently delayed the diagnosis by treating herself with salt. She had also carried on, probably for several years, without complaining of her symptoms.

Had I taken a good enough history? The diagnosis was in the history, and I had overlooked it. I had missed the fact she had lost weight, had been fainting, suffered abdominal pain and often felt sick. I had missed the salt craving.

The specialist gastroenterologist had missed the diagnosis by only concentrating on his speciality and focusing on the nausea and bowel symptoms, and by investigating her guts, which were normal. They had therefore reassured her there was nothing to find. The GP had not worked out the diagnosis – granted it would have been tricky to piece it all together in a 10-minute consultation, and then he would have had difficulty working out the most relevant specialist to refer the patient to. The doctors in the Emergency Department were wrong about the diagnosis, and they probably thought an 'eating disorder' wasn't strictly speaking an emergency. As their unit was always overburdened, they didn't welcome patients with chronic conditions who should be managed elsewhere. The specialist who might have made the diagnosis was the endocrinologist, but they only see patients in this guise once a condition is at least strongly suspected. The medical service in this country was an illogical system, one that had definitely evolved for the doctor's benefit rather than the patient's. Sadly, I was one of the last of the General Physicians, a rare breed that had been beaten down almost to extinction.

Hysterical Illness

'MUMMY FELL ASLEEP AGAIN,' Edward told Matthew.

I'd been tucked up in bed, reading a story to my youngest, when I'd drifted off in the middle of a page. I seldom stayed awake to finish story time and Edward usually crept out, turning the light off as he left.

I stirred, unsure whether I had the energy and motivation to get out of bed. I had wrestled through another restless night. Exhausted by 8 o'clock in the evening, I had retired to bed early. By midnight I had already slept for four hours and after that the tiniest noise would rouse me. I often woke with a start, my whole body suddenly jolting, as though I had fallen off a pavement, and my heart was trying to batter its way out of my chest. I felt hyper-alert. It was as if I was experiencing a panic attack or acute anxiety, only I wasn't anxious, worried or scared – I just wanted to sleep. Sometimes there was no noise, only a vivid dream or a disturbing thought that would reach my consciousness, and that was enough to set off the uncomfortable sensations. I felt permanently exhausted, each day waking up feeling unrefreshed.

I recalled a similar 'attack' years earlier. I went roller skating after several days of drinking too much alcohol, probably not eating sensibly, getting little sleep and being on my feet all day whilst wild oat roguing. This was a great job and involved walking through fields in a line and pulling any wild oats from the wheat crop. Back then I considered myself invincible.

I had been tired before leaving the house to go skating and should have declined the invite, but life was for living, wasn't it? Whilst circling the rink, though, I suddenly felt ghastly. I moved gingerly to the edge and then found a cool, dark corner, where I crouched quietly, unable to stop trembling. The banging in my chest and physical shakes were alarming, but I told myself it was just exhaustion.

There was another time, much more recently, when I had been called back into work. Having not been home long, after completing a busy 14-hour shift, I got changed and climbed into bed. The light in the bedroom was out and my body was in sleep mode, although my brain was still active, analysing the cases from the day. The telephone rang and my body suddenly had to switch back on again. I was needed in the hospital for an emergency. I dressed quickly and drove in, but halfway there I pulled over in a country lane, as I couldn't stop shaking and didn't feel safe enough to drive on.

I had reached the stage of having no appetite and no energy; each week I lost a little more weight. I felt depressed, tearful, agitated and restless, with fasciculations and a compulsion to keep moving. I had a constant tremor, not just in my hands, but my entire body. These were worse when I hadn't eaten for a short while. Sugar dissolved in water helped to relieve the shakes and also to clear my mind.

I felt let down by the medical profession. All my tests were normal and although the specialists I saw seemed to listen, they were only interested in their specialty and consequently only heard the symptoms that fitted with their field. For instance, the gastroenterologists weren't particularly worried about the extra-intestinal symptoms; the majority didn't listen to the systemic ones. Each specialist had their own piece of the puzzle, but to complete it all the pieces had to be in play. It felt as if no one believed me, which was compounded by the fact that every test, except for the CT scan, was normal. Each time I saw a specialist and was told the results of the tests were normal, it was as though I was supposed to suddenly feel reassured and get miraculously better. I was fed up with being told what I didn't have. This information did not make me feel better.

Even Matthew thought I had hysteria. After all, there was no confirmation that there was anything wrong with me. I don't blame him. He carried on as if there wasn't a problem; going on holidays with friends, attending meetings and pursuing all his hobbies. He struggled to accept that I was ill. It was almost as though by ignoring the issue the old me would return. He really just wanted me back. He longed for our old, slightly crazy family life together. I began to doubt myself, but the symptoms were so severe that how could they be psychosomatic? By this stage I was under hospital care and didn't see much of my GP. I reasoned that as I couldn't tie all the loose ends together after having hours to reflect on my symptoms, how could a GP reach any conclusions in just ten minutes? I figured they would just prescribe antidepressants, and I didn't plan on taking any, so it would simply be a waste of time. I didn't believe it was a mental illness. I wasn't anxious.

With no diagnosis, I wasn't able to take sick leave so I carried on working.

The Fall

'JO!' SISTER CALLED OUT. 'I need to have a word.' She ushered me into her office, which was conveniently positioned halfway along the corridor off the ward. With frosted glass panels it provided the perfect vantage point from which to oversee the steady traffic in and out.

Sister Hempson stood in the open doorway, hands on hips, observing me with her steely blue eyes as I walked into her office. As usual, she wore the dark blue dress that reflected her status as the senior nurse. She had been working in the hospital for over 30 years and we had been colleagues for 10. In all that time, I couldn't recall her ever speaking to me in this tone. I wondered whether someone had said something.

I sat in the corner of her office and looked out over the grey hospital car park and murky skies. Rain was lashing at the window and rivulets streamed down the pane. Trees were arching in the wind, which swirled between the blocks that made up the new hospital.

'Jo, are you all right?'

She knew. Someone must have told her. I had fallen on the ward. It was happening a lot recently. I was tripping over, or falling when going upstairs, and each time it happened I made the excuse that I must have misplaced my feet. I mentally listed the questions I would normally ask my patients and then told myself the answers. In my mind, I was being the patient *and* the doctor.

My inner voice was a running commentary, asking, 'Did I black out? Was I dizzy before I fell? Had I just stood up? Did my legs give way?'

I was impatient and frustrated with myself for not knowing the answers.

In truth, the questions were difficult to answer honestly. But how could I not know them? One second I was standing on the ward talking with someone and then . . . Perhaps I had moved awkwardly, or maybe I had turned my head too quickly when someone from behind me asked a question and lost my balance. That was it. How stupid!

'Well, did you hurt yourself?' Sister asked kindly. She was clearly waiting for an explanation.

I told her how silly I was, listed my excuses and said it was nothing. I could already feel the bruise on my cheek where my face had hit the wall. I could imagine how I must look; my pale, bruised, tear-stained face now blotchy with embarrassment from all the attention. I still couldn't stop trembling. The shaking, the crying, the falling – anyone would think I'd been drinking. It had become a frequent joke on the unit and in my mind I could hear the nurses mocking me.

Perhaps I should have acknowledged earlier that I was struggling, but I hadn't wanted to let my colleagues down. The ward was always incredibly busy and there had been vacant posts for several years, as they had struggled to recruit consultants and middle grades to work our demanding shifts.

I recognised that I had been working long hours in the hospital, and I would often carry on working in the evenings. At weekends I woke up early to finish paperwork. I'd always thrived on being busy, but I had been less efficient recently and things were taking me longer to complete. I was struggling to stay on top of my workload.

I eventually admitted to Sister Hempson that although I wasn't stressed or anxious, I was actually feeling dreadful and there was no clear explanation as to why. She told me I should take some time off as sick leave. But rather than being relieved, I felt guilty and upset. The routine of work had helped me pretend there wasn't a major problem, and by subconsciously following the same pattern each day I could keep up the charade.

The change being imposed on me made me uneasy. *How am I going to cope?* I thought. *Is there something physically wrong or am I insane?* I was becoming desperate and I needed answers.

★

Away from the regular pattern of work, I deteriorated. I even had difficulty driving. I probably should have acknowledged this earlier than I did, but I couldn't be certain when it had started. There was no problem on familiar routes, so I was able to find my way to the children's school, but if it was a journey I hadn't driven for a while I found that I didn't know the way. Like everything, there had been such a gradual deterioration and variation in my ability to function that it was difficult to be sure when it started to become a real issue.

On one occasion, before I stopped work, I drove to the Deanery for a training meeting and found that the key fob to the car wouldn't work. I kept pressing, but the car doors wouldn't open. Assuming it was a problem with the fob mechanism, I tried the button to open the boot. I was wondering how I was going to clamber into the car through the boot when I was startled by a noise from behind. The boot of the car on the other side of the car park was wide open. It took me a while to realise that I had been trying to get into the wrong vehicle. I hadn't remembered where I had parked the car.

It was a silly mistake, which I'm sure everyone has made at one time or another. Only my 'silly mistakes' were becoming more and more frequent. I seemed unable to recognise landmarks and would process road signs too late, feeling unsure whether or not it was the correct turning. Even familiar routes were becoming difficult to navigate. I was suffering with paroxysm of indecisiveness. On the back route to the supermarket, there was one left turn. I knew it was a left turn, but I couldn't remember where to take it. Was it the turning with houses, or the one with a hedge and a signpost? I would either end up in the recreation ground – seeing the swings I knew I had turned too early – or drive past and have to take the longer route, feeling cross with myself for being so stupid. Tom would direct whenever he was in the car with me. At nine, he had an incredible memory for roads, even if he had only been to a particular location once before.

I recall trying to take the children to a friend's house 20-minutes away by car. Matthew had been keen to get some exercise and had cycled there. The friend was Taf, my aforementioned bedroom intruder. Medicine has this habit of throwing you back in contact with old acquaintances and he and Matthew had ended up working in the same hospital. A decade later and Taf was now married with children. He was no longer the prankster and was serious about his work and family.

Unfortunately, the journey to Taf's house took over an hour because I became hopelessly lost in the Norfolk countryside. By the time I arrived I was shaking uncontrollably. I emerged from the car and slammed the door with gusto, feeling frustrated, cross and upset. I tried to walk away from the car and couldn't. There was something holding me back. I tried again but still couldn't move. I looked round, feeling confused, and saw that I had slammed my fingers in the car door. Worst of all was the fact I couldn't feel them. It was scary. Clearly there was something very wrong. I could *not* explain this one away. I struggled through lunch, not wanting the children or our kind hosts to see my tear-drenched eyes. The meal dragged on. I feigned smiles, but I was distracted. Fighting back my emotions was difficult because at that moment I knew I had to face up to it. It was as though I suddenly couldn't pretend any more. I was ill.

Driving at night was even worse. I struggled to see in the dark and trying to mentally process the different lights was also difficult. It was almost impossible to work out where the slip roads were. However, it wasn't just the dark and the lights, I also hated switching cars. I'd get cross if Matthew took my car and he couldn't understand why, thinking I was being unreasonable. It would usually end with him despairing at me and me bursting into tears. It was months later when I realised the reason I struggled was that in Matthew's car I wasn't certain where the pedals were. I would try to look down to find them. It was as if I didn't know where my feet were. On several occasions I pressed on the accelerator instead of the brake pedal.

From then on things started happening at an alarming rate. I picked up a pan straight from the AGA and my fingers immediately blistered, though I felt absolutely nothing. I wore a new pair of shoes, which felt as though they fitted well, but when I removed them at the end of the day I discovered large blisters. Scratching an itch on my skin left gorged-out, painless holes, which took weeks to heal and often wept. I noticed I wasn't sweating. My feet were dry even in summer. When the children complained about rank odours coming from the countryside, the fridge or their brother, I was unable to smell them.

I lost my confidence socially. I wasn't able to recognise people. If they clearly knew me I had to pretend. It was embarrassing and even more so when, on one occasion, someone pretended to know me. Because I didn't want the shame of admitting to not knowing who he was, I went along with the pretence, laughing and chatting. He thought I was egging him on, encouraging him, flirting. It became clear from something he said that we were actually complete strangers, and perhaps my response had been overly friendly. My naturally outgoing personality meant I could usually cover-up for lapses in memory. Now my mind wasn't quick enough to cope with even the most basic conversation. I was so angry with him, and with myself. To avoid this kind of dilemma in the future, I avoided everyone except close family and friends.

Hypoglycaemia

I STARTED TRYING TO WORK OUT WHAT was wrong with me, whilst thinking about the past. Over the years I had developed some odd symptoms.

2000

Off work on maternity leave, whilst heavily pregnant with Tom, I took the girls swimming. Emily and Anna were both toddlers, preferring to splash in the warm, shallow, dimly lit 'baby' pool. By the windows, overlooking the outdoor pool, I observed a boy of about 10. He was crouching on his own at the side of the water, looking lonely and bored. I thought how surely he must have rather been splashing and playing with the other children. His mother was in the water. She had been swimming, although I hadn't seen her doing lengths. The boy was trying to say something to her and it looked as if he wanted them both to leave the pool. He resembled a faithful dog not wanting to leave its owner, but unsure of what action to take. The mother wasn't paying much attention to the boy; in fact, she was just holding onto the side of the pool. Looking at him more carefully, I could see that his bland, pallid facial expression was not caused by disinterest – he was afraid. Something terrible appeared to be happening.

It all seemed to take place in slow motion. I waddled to the side of the main pool. The lady was unresponsive, although incredibly, she was still clinging to the side of the pool. She appeared to be floating, but for how much longer I couldn't ascertain. I realised that with my cumbersome shape I was in no state to haul her out of the pool, so I had to just hold onto her and stop her falling into the water. Meanwhile, Emily and Anna had become curious and had followed me to the water's edge.

'Mummy, she sleep?' Emily asked, probably wondering why anyone would choose to go to sleep in a swimming pool.

She was asleep, deeply so – in fact, she was unconscious. After what seemed like an age, I finally managed to secure the attention of the lifeguard and the lady was lifted out of the water to safety. She was given hypostop (sugary paste), which was squirted into her mouth, and I waited with the pool staff until the ambulance arrived, offering comfort to the young boy. His mother had diabetes and had obviously become hypoglycaemic whilst swimming. Hypoglycaemia occurs when the usual protective mechanisms – hunger, shakiness, sweating – to alert the person that their blood sugar is low stop being effective. This happens in some patients with diabetes and can be dangerous if they continue to drive, or swim, as with little or no warning they can become unconscious.

Some years earlier, I had admitted to the unit a patient with profound hypoglycaemia who was in a deep coma. Upon examining her, I found she had markedly abnormal reflexes. These reflexes are the spontaneous movements of the body, which can be triggered by certain stimuli, such as stroking or scratching the bottom of the feet or using a hammer to stretch the tendons. When the bottom of the feet are scratched, the toes are meant to point down – like a classic ballerina's pose – but if the toes point up – as in contemporary dance – it can indicate a stroke. I was convinced this lady would have permanent brain damage, particularly when the next day, and the day after when she was awake, she still had the abnormal reflexes suggestive of a stroke. Hypoglycaemia can cause coma, permanent brain damage and even death, but incredibly, in this instance, the derangement was slowly reversible. The patient had not suffered a stroke. The abnormal neurological findings were all due to the low blood glucose. The brain recovered fully and the nerve cells started to function again.

The usual symptoms of hypoglycaemia include sweating, lightheadedness, blurred vision, palpitations, anxiety and shaking. Some patients will feel hungry or crave food or sugar.

I remember non-diabetic patients telling me they developed 'low blood sugar' in the afternoons and had to snack. Usually it was the patients who struggled with their weight. I didn't understand their complaints, as the sugar level wouldn't actually be low, but nevertheless, they seemed to describe the symptoms of hypoglycaemia accurately.

★

Thinking about my symptoms, I had noticed the tremor, but I didn't pay any real attention to it until a colleague, assessing me in clinic, mentioned it in the months after the fall. 'How long have you had that?' he enquired in a business-like manner.

I couldn't answer the question.

Thinking back, I tried to remember when it had first started, but I had no idea. It was just there. I admitted to myself that I hadn't really focused on the tremor, as there had been other symptoms I was more worried about. I had been getting palpitations, and I realised that the tremor often occurred with these sensations of banging in my chest. It was noticeably worse when I hadn't eaten, and it had also been more troublesome at the end of a day at work. It seemed to be associated with the fog in my brain and also extreme fatigue. I remembered taking a break in the doctors' office in the middle of a shift and not knowing if I could muster the energy for the remainder of the stint. Interestingly, the tremor and fog would ease if I ate sugar. I started craving chocolate in the afternoons to give me the energy to continue working. I would then add a sachet of sugar to a mug of tea, then two, then three. I was becoming addicted to sugar. It wasn't something I owned up to, as I didn't need to confess – no one ever asks how much sugar you consume.

The palpitations were odd. The pulse wasn't rapid, but the fluttering sensation in my chest was disquieting. I could alleviate them by applying gentle pressure to the side of my neck. I knew I was performing a so-called 'vagal manoeuvre'. I had often done this to patients with rapid heart rates to slow the heart rate or even flip their abnormal rhythm back to a normal, sinus rhythm. Even though I did not have an arrhythmia, pressure on my neck calmed the palpitations.

I was baffled. Like my patients, I seemed to be suffering with episodes that mimicked 'low blood sugar', and eating anything sugary helped. The symptoms of hypoglycaemia are deeply entrenched in our genetic makeup and designed to get the fight or flight (sympathetic) response operating on full blast. The system is in place to ensure that we get food as quickly as possible to correct the deficit. We feel hungry, or light-headed, or lacking in energy, and we go to the fridge to get a snack, or we add sugar to our tea. The vagal manoeuvre opposes the sympathetic response, stimulating the housekeeping response and acting to return all systems to normal function. I was sure I didn't have hypoglycaemia, but I seemed to be suffering with an overactive fight or flight response, and my symptoms were also corrected by sugar.

Café Game

2010

I WAS AT HOME ON LEAVE FROM THE HOSPITAL. Lacking the structure of work, my days seemed endless. I filled the time aimlessly writing lists and reminiscing. I occasionally ventured out of the house into town, where I waited for the children to finish school. I sat in cafés, looked out of the window and observed passers-by.

It was strange how clearly I could remember events from years ago, but not things that had happened just a few hours earlier. Reflecting on the past was like looking at old photographs. The memory was lightly misted at the edges, but in contrast the colours and scents were still vivid. I would close my eyes and remember happy times with my nana, clearly picturing her house: the garden in full flower, with cottage garden favourites – cornflowers, granny's bonnets (*aquilegia*), love-in-a-mist (*nigella*), hollyhocks and nasturtiums. There were also rock fumewort (*Corydalis lutea*), with their bright green feathery foliage. I thought the flowers resembled yellow toothbrushes. It grew everywhere, in every crevice.

1976

As a child I was often ill. I was particularly weak and thin after succumbing to chickenpox. My parents could not take any more time off work to look after me, so I was dispatched to the other side of the country to Nana's house. Nana was a retired teacher. An eccentric with firmly fixed ideas, she was a vegetarian who ate nut roast and lentil burgers. She believed in complimentary medicine, life after death, and the abolishment of nuclear arms. One Christmas, she even bolted herself to the fence at Greenham Common, whilst the rest of the family were eating roast turkey.

Nana's house was always cold and the beds had heavy layers of blankets and eiderdowns. A hot water bottle was essential and once the part of the bed you were lying on had warmed up you dared not move and risk the blast of cold air. One year there was even ice on the inside of the window.

Nana knew exactly how to restore me to full health and there would be no disagreeing with the therapy. I was told to walk around the orchard every morning, taking deep breaths – I had to breathe in for a count of eight and then out for the same amount of time. On the first few attempts I found it exhausting, and only managed to count to three or four.

'I can't do it!' I protested to Nana.

'Nonsense! There's no such word as can't,' she replied in her matter-of-fact manner.

I was sent out the following day, obediently breathing in and out deeply whilst counting to eight, doubtful of Nana's methods. But then I started to enjoy being outside and began to take an interest in the apple trees and chickens. I helped pick up the bundles of sticks after pruning and fed the chickens every morning, collecting the eggs later on each day. The chickens roamed free within the 'Dingley Dell', the name we used for the large hollow in the orchard; the chicken sheds were arranged on the crest of the slope, with small doors opening to where the chickens laid the eggs. It was exciting opening up each trap door to find the smooth, brown eggs, still warm to the touch.

In the afternoons, Nana insisted I wrote a diary. She had a motto: 'Only your best is good enough for you.' It meant that even if you failed, as long as you tried your best then you couldn't have done any more. I sat on a high stool at the breakfast bar in Nana's cosy kitchen. The kitchen was the activity hub in the house. It was always bright and warm, being heated by a solid fuel range and having walls painted in primrose yellow, with the floor and curtains gold-orange. It felt as though the sun shone from within this room. In fact, there was an inner energy radiating throughout the entire house. On my work station there was a red, ceramic donkey, decorated in flowers. There were two houseplants climbing the walls, one on the archway between the dining and kitchen areas. Jars of pulses filled the shelf and homemade bread was kept on a wooden board. A clock ticked loudly above me.

My diary was made of yellow card folded in two to make a booklet. I worked hard decorating the edges of the card with felt tip pens and writing each diary entry on paper that Nana had lined for me and then stuck in. I drew pictures to annotate the diary: the orchard, the hens, a basket of eggs and primroses. Sometimes Nana played games with me. The worst game was the 'Sock Game', which involved washing Granddad's socks using a washboard.

Nana's property had four dwellings comprising two pairs of semi-detached cottages. She had bought them at a time when owning property was not the profitable, money-making venture it has become. She was more interested in the potential and in the project it presented, rather than in any monetary value.

The first two adjoining cottages had been knocked into one, but this had taken place in stages. Each time I visited, it was exciting to find out what was new. I'd climb up two sets of stairs into the attic, before coming down another set that led into the back room. As a child, I thought that all houses should have more than one staircase. It made them far more interesting.

The attic was a treasure trove of paper, paints, craft material, ribbons, lace and buttons. Nana was creative. The surfaces were cluttered with her drawings and paintings of various scenes. My favourite was of the orchard, with apple blossom decorating the trees in delicate shades of pink and white. Nana took me to an art class where they were drawing still life and I drew an apple in pastels. Not content with the readily available craft materials, I spent hours in Nana's flowerbed digging up the pasty coloured, sticky garden clay, which lay in clumps below the surface. I would make clay pots and clay fruit. I even created a clay fried breakfast, painting them with poster paints once they had baked hard in the sun. I remembered the confusion one visit when I arrived at Nana's to find myself in a deep cupboard – one of the sets of stairs to the attic had disappeared.

In the 'Café Game', Nana and I would sit facing each other in the bay window overlooking the garden and pretend we were sitting at a table in a café, looking out at a busy high street. The orchard was beyond the honeysuckle-smothered hedge. Clay fried eggs were easy for me to imagine, but made-up people were more difficult for my seven-year-old mind to picture, when the only busy thing I could see was a bee frantically visiting every honeysuckle flower. Nana was wonderfully creative at this game. She would describe women dressed in their finery walking their matching poodles, men in top hats clicking their polished shoes on the street in time to their ebony walking sticks; she pictured faces, hairdos, clothes, hats and jewellery, but more importantly she recounted mannerisms, characteristics and afflictions. I was intrigued, as one of Nana's sayings was, 'You can't judge a book by its cover', but she wasn't judging, she was observing. I was less confident when relating my own characters, tending to stick to colours, patterns, shapes and sizes.

I loved Christmas at Nana's – the glowing fire from behind the grate in the cosy sitting room with the dark red velvet curtains; the hand-painted murals of the figures from the 12 days of Christmas decorating the walls up the stairway; the whole family sitting together, laughing and reminiscing; the excitement of the unopened presents and Nana's homemade bread. Nana was killed aged 64 by a drunk driver. A few years after her death, a violent storm uprooted many of the old apple trees in the top orchard where I had wandered picking up sticks. I missed my visits. I had so few photos of her, only memories, her necklace of ceramic beads and some of her paintings.

2010

From the window of the café, I could look out over the striped roofs of the market stalls opposite, which were like deckchairs on a beach. The lines weren't clear today so I turned to face away from the blur. The market was in the town centre and was always a hub of activity. I wondered what I would describe now in an imaginary café overlooking a garden: rotund individuals; waddling gaits; stomachs protruding like twin pregnancies, even in the men; short skirts revealing thunder thighs; trousers worn low to reveal butt cleavage; sallow complexions;

pockmarked skin and treble chins. I would definitely remark on the sheer size of the individuals – wherever I looked there were oversized people. It had become endemic.

I might also have described the copious amounts of sweet, sugary snacks on sale in the cafés and stores. The chocolates and sugar-laden drinks on display by the checkouts, the sandwiches on offer as a meal deal so that it was actually cheaper to buy the fizzy drink and cookie together with the sandwich than the healthier option of the solo sandwich. Who was going to be strong-willed enough to take the offer and bin the cookie and drink (or even pay a little more)? When selecting fast food, it had become difficult to eat healthily. Only a few fast food stores offered a selection of fresh vegetables to take out. Admittedly, there were salads, but even they were often dripping with syrup-infused dressing.

There was evidence everywhere of how people's shapes and sizes had changed. A display I'd seen at the Victoria and Albert Museum in London showcased fashion throughout the ages, revealing the tiny frames in the mid-sixteenth century, before sugar. Even in the sixties (just after the post-war food restrictions), minis had been the fashion, Twiggy having the model figure that all girls envied.

I wondered whether doctors had lost the power of observation. I imagined I was a certain person observing the passers-by. The man I thought of was James Parkinson, a widely published and politically active apothecary and surgeon. In 1817, he published descriptions of a small number of his patients with a 'shaking palsy'.[4] He was the first person to document the coexistence of several symptoms and signs of a condition he called 'Paralysis Agitans'. He described the cardinal signs: a resting tremor, a stooped posture and a shuffling gait. In short, he identified a distinct disease that was progressive, untreatable and with no known cause. He was describing a 'syndrome'.

Sitting in the café, playing Nana's game, I realised that she had taught me to observe, while practising medicine had taught me to reflect on these observations. There is no doubt that medical progress has been made by advances in technology, but some of the most important discoveries have been made simply by looking and thinking.

Empty Calories

2008

MY FATHER CAME TO VISIT. Even though we'd lived in the house for over two years, this was the first time he'd been over. Matthew and I bought our country cottage planning to extend it. It was a major undertaking and although it wasn't the first time we had taken on such a project, this was on a much bigger scale. The original cottage would have had two rooms downstairs and two upstairs, but it had been extended unsympathetically back in the 1980s. There was room to extend further to create a family kitchen in the adjacent pantiled barn, which would better suit our modern life. Dad had bought a new house at about the same time as us, which is why we hadn't seen much of him. I was pleased he had finally got to see the house and was proud of what we had achieved so far. We planned to join the cottage to the L-shaped barn, which would create an enclosed, south-facing courtyard. The plans had been drafted, but with us both working full-time and the four children, there never seemed to be enough time. I had planted bulbs in the late autumn, using a head torch, and now there were bright daffodils bobbing in the orchard. Around the orchard and the vegetable patch, Matthew had planted a beech hedge, but it was too early to tell if the whips had survived.

I particularly wanted my father's opinion on the front wall of the old cottage. He was extremely knowledgeable on an incredibly diverse range of subjects, reading up on things like quantum physics and Darwin's theories of evolution for pleasure. In his spare time, he had also rebuilt several houses. Matthew was worried about a new crack in the upstairs bedroom and thought there might be some subsidence. There was a tall larch tree standing aloof and proud relatively close to the weather-beaten cottage, and there had been some freak storms and dry winters.

'Jo, I wouldn't worry. They are settling cracks, only plaster deep,' my father reassured me. 'These old buildings creak but aren't likely to fall down.'

Dad obviously wasn't concerned. As this part of the building had stood firm for the past 200 years, it was apparently safe. I hoped Matthew would be reassured too.

My dad wasn't a builder by trade; in fact, he had worked for the Meat and Livestock Commission (MLC) from just after I was born. The MLC had been set up shortly before he joined it, following the Agriculture Act in 1967. Against ever increasing media and public antipathy, he spent his entire working life promoting British meat and animal products. Red meat was considered healthy in my childhood home, butter good for you – it was all a matter of quantities. Nothing should be consumed to excess, including alcohol, although when it came to red wine my dad didn't strictly adhere to this rule!

I recall an intense, late discussion once over a bottle of wine. 'Animal science is so much more advanced,' Dad said. 'You doctors don't see it, though.'

It was about the time that HIV had been identified, which led to an almost hysterical fear of the virus. Dad surmised that these viruses were extremely clever and that they may even spell the downfall of the human race. He had probably just finished reading Stephen Hawking's latest science revelation. He didn't quite get to the point of insinuating that viruses would take over the world, but an army of miniature terrestrial invaders came to mind – perhaps I had just drunk too much red wine that night!

Dad also lamented that although the agricultural industry had the means to feed the world, political and human factors prevented this from happening. He could not understand why anyone in the present day should starve.

★

Whilst training, I hadn't really understood the significance of vitamins. (This was despite working in Cambridge, where scientists at the Dunn Nutrition Unit, which was set up after World War II to explore nutritional problems arising from measures such as rationing, played a key role in the early work on vitamins.) An understanding of specific vitamin deficiencies was only a minor part of my medical degree; the discovery of each of these, although interesting, was more a study of the history of medicine. In the past, there had been major problems with poor nutrition. Diseases such as rickets, due to vitamin D deficiency, and scurvy, as a result of vitamin C deficiency, had been rife. Now that supplements were so readily available and food was plentiful and fortified these diseases have been eradicated. Many years later, I found out that one of the early researchers at the Dunn Unit was John Yudkin, who had been primarily interested in the effects of dietary vitamins. He had incredible insight into the importance of social issues, nutrition and public health. He was interested not only in the diseases associated with poverty, but also those linked with affluence. Whilst I was in Cambridge, the Dunn Unit was renamed the MRC (Medical Research Council)

Human Nutrition Research Unit. Its original aims were then broadened and, put simply, were: what to eat, how much to eat, what effect food has on health, and which diseases are caused by bad nutrition.

My fellow gastroenterology colleague, Heather, arranged to conduct some research in the unit. It was expected that trainees in medicine, as opposed to surgery, would undertake a period of research, particularly when working in an establishment such as Cambridge. However, jokes were often made about Heather's project, which was to investigate the bacterial flora and gas production in faeces. It was common knowledge that the worst job in the hospital was working on the 'hot stool bench', looking through fresh turd for ova (eggs), cysts of parasites, or the worms themselves. I couldn't understand why anyone would actually choose to pick through poo or, for that matter, conduct experiments on flatus! But Heather's aim wasn't to explore the nutritional value of food, she was actually measuring the gases produced in patients with inflammatory conditions of the large bowel (colon). The specific disease she was investigating was known as ulcerative colitis, and her aim was to explore the gas production in response to certain food types.

At the time, this had seemed odd to me, as I had been taught that ulcerative colitis, like many conditions with the suffix '-itis' was due to inflammation, and such illnesses responded to steroids or cortisone. I had, therefore, learnt that dermatitis or eczema (skin inflammation), arthritis (joint inflammation) and vasculitis (inflammation of the blood vessels) all responded to steroids. Thus, so did colitis. I had thought it strange how Heather was proposing that the abnormal gases were due to an alteration in bacteria in the large bowel. It did not tally with my understanding that the condition was due to inflammation. If colitis were due to infection then surely antibiotic treatment would be more appropriate?

Certain doctors in Cambridge were using a very restricted diet or even a liquid nutritional supplement to treat patients with Crohn's disease, which was another inflammatory condition of the gut. I had witnessed patients treated successfully with this supplement and had to admit, with some reservation, that the liquid food seemed to be effective. There was one memorable patient who was admitted on multiple occasions whilst I was there. Each time this poor lad had a severe exacerbation of Crohn's disease, presenting with deep, painful ulceration throughout his gut, although it predominantly affected his oesophagus and mouth. I remembered he also had terrible skin, which was pockmarked with weeping sores that wouldn't heal, and a moon face from the large doses of steroids he had to take. The specialist team of nurses started him on the liquid supplements and his condition always improved. But if he gave in and ate chocolate it would almost certainly cause a relapse.

I was unable to explain how chocolate could cause this much disease, or how bacteria could have this effect on a patient's guts, without at least someone managing to find the offending germ. Likewise, treating patients with diet alone made no sense.

In my final year of specialist training, I was sent on a nutrition course. I didn't manage to conduct research, as Heather had done, and I had no specialist skill to offer to a gastroenterology department. However, because there was a renewed interest in nutrition within the field of gastroenterology, the training body decided that this was to be my area of specialist interest. I was determined not to find the course interesting or necessary, as the timing had been dreadful: it was a week-long residential course and attendance was mandatory if I was to become a consultant. The members of the all-male training body gave me no choice. I thought the decision was insensitive, as they had failed to take into account the fact I had four children under the age of seven. By going on the course, I would be away for Edward's first birthday.

Despite my apprehension, I found the course stimulating, discovering that obesity is linked to the number of television sets in a household, which supported the fact that being very overweight is associated with inactivity. However, I was more impressed by the fact that the beginning of the obesity epidemic actually coincided with the end of food rationing in the early 1950s, bringing an influx of sugar that affected the next generations.

The focus of the course was specifically about the link between blood cholesterol and coronary heart disease. I learnt that even obese people are malnourished. I initially thought I must have misheard, disbelieving that it was possible to eat too much and still be short of a vital constituent, but I discovered that obese patients have deficiencies in some micronutrients and are often iron deficient, too. I also learnt how difficult it is to conduct any study looking into the effect of nutrition, as diets vary extensively and self-reporting is notoriously inaccurate. At the time, I had thought the course was well run. In hindsight, I realise that I hadn't been encouraged to think for myself, and that they hadn't given me the original work to analyse and critique.

I tried to discover the science behind the low-fat dietary recommendations that had changed nutrition guidelines in recent decades. In the 1950s, Ancel Keys, an American physiologist, was interested in the effect of diet on health, and he published the 'Seven Countries Study[5]', which showed that in seven countries (the USA, Finland, Yugoslavia, the

Netherlands, Italy, Greece and Japan) blood cholesterol levels were strongly related to coronary heart disease. He showed that in these countries, those with the highest saturated fat consumption had the highest rates of heart disease. In 1961, the American Heart Association released guidelines to restrict saturated fat and cholesterol, including beef, due to its association with heart disease. Hence the start of the low-fat diet campaign and, shortly afterwards, my father's role promoting British meat produce. The cholesterol hypothesis was reinforced in the 1990s, when the introduction of drugs to reduce cholesterol actually reduced cardiovascular disease. It all seemed to make sense.

The recognised association between animal fat intake and death from cardiovascular causes has altered eating habits for generations of people. However, the analysis has been criticised, as out of the 22 countries involved in the study only seven were selected and used in the final report. Countries such as France, where traditionally people have a diet with a higher fat content, were excluded. The diet consumed during the study period was subsequently said to be unrepresentative of the general population in France.

I tried to analyse the original data using a graph that had been published online.[4] I redrew the graph, with the original y-axis as the coronary heart disease deaths per 100,000 population. I plotted this against the proximity from the equator on the x-axis. Using Keys' mortality figures, there seemed to be an association between the degrees latitude (north or south) and the mortality from coronary heart disease. There were clusters of countries close to each other geographically with a similar death rate; for example, Austria, Denmark, Germany and Switzerland. In fact, the line, which passed through most of the scattered points on the graph, was exponential rather than straight, with a benefit of living in sunnier climates. Despite this there were distinct outliers, which were way off the curve: the USA, Australia and Israel.

Keys made the observation that there were many people living in Southern Italy surviving to a hundred years of age. He spent almost three decades living there himself and died in 2004, having reached his hundredth year. He showed that there was a lower incidence of heart disease in the countries (in olive growing regions) that used olive oil as the main fat, the so-called 'Mediterranean diet', which he also popularised. I remembered a lecture at medical school informing me that immigrants acquire the disease profile of the country they move to. I was told this was due to the different diet they consumed in their new country. This may be true, but many people continue to eat the same food, persisting with cultures and traditions. Therefore, this might suggest that geographical location is more relevant.

There were a number of diets available during the mid twentieth century to aid weight loss, but John Yudkin promoted the idea, with plausible evidence, that by restricting dietary carbohydrates weight could be controlled. He was best known for his epidemiological studies demonstrating that in many countries there was an association between sugar intake and the incidence of coronary heart disease. He worked out that as carbohydrate restriction in obese patients caused them to lose weight, high-carbohydrate consumption was the most likely cause of excessive weight. Yudkin's studies on total fat and animal fat produced conflicting results and showed no conclusive evidence to link coronary heart disease with fat intake. He concluded that there was a relationship between coronary heart disease and sugar intake, but also between coronary heart disease and lifestyle choices, particularly reduced exercise.

Sugar is an obvious culprit, as it provides calories with no nutritional value – there are no vitamins, no nitrogen or phosphate for making proteins, and no trace elements, which are important in the chemical synthetic reactions in the body. Sugar provides empty, excessive calories to the majority of individuals on the planet. Calories are useful if you are burning them by exercising at full capacity, but many of us are barely using up anything above what it requires to breathe, talk and digest our food. Sugar is useful only as a means of transporting energy around a creature or plant. All living cells are capable of making sugar in sufficient quantities; organisms do not need to ingest it in order to survive.

Fifty years ago, Yudkin wrote an article clearly defining sugar's contribution to several diseases, including obesity, diabetes mellitus, tooth decay and myocardial infarction (heart attack). He suggested that the excessive consumption of sugar might result in a disturbance in the secretion of insulin, which in turn might contribute to atherosclerosis (the underlying disease process in the blood vessels in cardiovascular disease) and diabetes.

I thought back to the first few cases of Parkinson's disease. James Parkinson spent most of his working life in Shoreditch, in the East End of London. The population of the capital had expanded rapidly and pollution was rife. In 1802, the West India Dock opened, enabling huge quantities of sugar to be imported and stored. Could Parkinson's disease be another condition affected by sugar?

Black Diary

BY NOW, MATTHEW WAS DOING MOST of the cooking at home.

'What's this?' Emily asked, as we sat down for supper one evening. I had a bowl of pumpkin soup, whilst the others were eating a curry that Matthew had prepared. My husband was suspiciously quiet, but the meal was a success and Tom even had seconds. I stayed at the table whilst the others cleared up around me.

'We've lost one of the apple trees,' Matthew said, as he wiped the table clean. 'I've asked Bob to take it down,' he added, and then carried on talking about the plans for the garden and the vegetable plot.

Bob was the gardener and he had been helping us for years. With both Matthew and I working, it was too large a plot to maintain between us. I heard Matthew's words, but had no interest. I was immersed in a world lacking warmth or feeling. A place where it was permanently winter and *none* of the trees had any life. I felt cold all the time. In particular, my hands and feet were like blocks of ice, even in the middle of summer. I used two hot water bottles, one for my hands and one for my feet, partly to keep warm, but also because of the burning pains I was experiencing.

It had been months since the fall and I was steadily deteriorating whilst on leave at home. I had started to drop things. The children were helping out more at meal times, preferring not to have supper served in their lap. I regularly tripped up and toppled over. I wasn't sure whether I had weakness from loss of muscle strength or ataxia (loss of coordination and balance), or whether I had lost proprioception (the nerves telling you where the parts of your body are). I was falling over repeatedly, unable to right myself.

The children left the kitchen to finish their homework and switch on the television. Matthew then proudly admitted that the curry was made using the 'venison' from the freezer. I had completely forgotten about the deer in the swimming pool and it had slipped my mind to remove the body parts, as planned.

'It's perfectly good,' said Matthew, clearly proud of his resourcefulness. 'It just needed to be slow cooked.'

★

Christmas Day at home with close family was a low point. Darkness controlled me. Sombre thoughts permeated my mind, as a sea fret creeps over marshes, chilling me. It was numbing, emotionally and physically. If I occupied myself I could block out the desperation, but that required energy and I was exhausted. Once the thoughts descended it was difficult to escape the gloom. Now alone in my room, the silent voices vented their malicious message:

'Do it!'

After lunch, barely able to eat any of it, I slipped back to bed. It had rained all day. Through the floorboards, I could hear the melancholy notes of a Chopin nocturne and the cheerful chattering of children. Edward and Tom were chasing each other and Anna, who had helped to clear away Christmas lunch, was now probably listening to music or online. Emily was playing the piano.

Through my window I could see the black barn, silhouetted in late afternoon light, set apart from the house by a concrete standing. It creaked in the wind. In the gusts the roof panels lifted and the guttering shook. Inside the barn lay dusty cables, empty bottles, rusty machinery and oily spare parts, relics from the previous owner's failed business.

In my mind I could picture the inside of the barn. Loose hay drifted ghost-like in the draft. The concrete floor had once been painted, but it was now faded except for those patches cleaned and brightened by rain leaking through the roof, a reminder that with care the barn still could have life and be useful. It was dim inside, few of the strip lights worked and pale winter light found its way through a gap in a panel, highlighting dancing dust motes – a random, purposeless motion, like my attempts at thinking.

Previously, I had felt inspired to transform this space, but truthfully I now realised that it was nothing but a clutter trap. With me out of action, the mess had accumulated. Amongst the bicycles, a ride-on tractor and a wooden boat, a washing line was strung from one side of the barn to the other. A cricket ball hung on an elastic rope suspended in mid air, as though life stood still. A metal shelf was stacked haphazardly with old paint tins, tools and plant pots – there were containers and boxes filled with weed killer and slug pellets, as well as various toxins and poisons.

The contents of the barn were all too familiar, and my thoughts seemed to beckon me out to the desolate building.

The rope, the washing line, or poison, no one needs to know. Your life is worthless, you are worthless, useless, suffering needlessly, no hope of recovery, put an end to the misery, do it, while you still can, do it now!'

★

As I became more unwell and less confident talking to people, I began to write in a small black notebook with grey-lined pages, which I kept by my bedside. I felt muddled and unable to express my thoughts verbally, as though there was cotton wool filling my skull, blunting any brain activity. I tried to shake my head or prop it up, as it felt disconnected and heavy, but this didn't help. Jotting notes in the black diary gave me a feeling of order and sense, although the scribbles were sketchy and shaky.

I spent hours awake each night searching online. At the front of the book, I made notes on the scientific papers I was working through, researching the relationship between exercise, obesity and the metabolic syndrome. I acknowledged that doing so was a mental exercise to reinstate a sense of purpose. I couldn't concentrate on a novel, as I would forget the characters and the story, rereading the same paragraph again and again. Somehow I was still able to read an abstract, make notes and feel as though I still had my faculties. I read and reread multiple papers, often forgetting the ones I had already studied.

The back of the diary consisted of rambling thoughts that served as a marker of my condition as I deteriorated. I had good days, often after resting, and bad days, mostly after a period of minimal exertion, such as attending a hospital appointment. I found it difficult to sit still and relax, as I had an incomprehensible compulsion to keep moving, even though I was aware that I was achieving very little. It was as though keeping active made me feel less jittery.

Already feeling tearful at the slightest provocation, pain in hands on trying to hold anything — pen, phone — feeling shaky and tired — feet ache across dorsum, but also burn when seated, pain extending to my calves but have walked the length of the hospital today.

Walking through town I feel bitter, full of hate and negative. The rain doesn't help. I can converse on a one-to-one basis but don't seek conversation. Driving home, I am aware of more severe pains, particularly in my feet while using the pedals in the car. It seems to radiate up the lateral aspect of my right lower leg. Once at home I have a purpose — the children's supper, but I am irritable and intolerant of their usual bickering.

I doubted I would ever find out what was wrong with me. I knew there was a severe problem, I had some form of ailment, but even if they worked out that I had a degenerative condition, the chance of it being curable was remote. I was facing years of being dependent and having no quality of life. I didn't want to be a burden any more. I didn't want to live like this. It was as though I didn't care for myself. I was scared of myself.

The rope, the barn, the top field, kitchen knife, sleep forever, peace…

Beriberi

2011

I HAD AN EXTREMELY POOR QUALITY of life for months, and lost hope of ever recovering. During this time, if I'd been without the support of family and friends, or if I had been inclined to seek an escape or to resort to substance abuse, my resolve would undoubtedly have wavered. I investigated the scientific papers, but in my desperation to find an explanation, I also read online forums. I learnt about the symptoms other patients with malrotation were experiencing.

> 'I have congenital malrotation of the gut and feel unwell, with difficulty eating. I feel sure I need an operation, but my doctor says surgery isn't indicated.'

> 'I feel tired all the time and dreadful. I'm losing weight.'

I felt sorry for these distressed individuals, who were resorting to any means to try to get help. It seemed no one in the medical profession was listening to them, either. Each evening I lulled myself to sleep with my tablet, searching through data on random websites. I would relate my newest discovery over porridge the next morning. Most mornings, Matthew would nod whilst continuing to read the latest financial update on his own tablet. I studied anything and everything related vaguely or more intricately to my symptoms, but it wasn't until I read up on beriberi, which causes falls and painful feet, that I knew I'd found the answer I had been searching for.

Fraser, a colleague at work, had pointed at me on the unit several months earlier.

'Eh! Whit ye neid is thiaminn,' he said in his Scottish drawl.

I had lost a lot of weight and thiamine, or vitamin B1, is what is given to patients with anorexia nervosa – a condition where weight loss becomes uncontrollable. Except that I didn't have anorexia! I was controlling my food intake to ensure that I could eat enough, attempting to retain my weight with a 'soup and smoothie' diet. I found that solid food caused obstruction, but by supping soups and smoothies all day, I was able to take in enough nourishment. Porridge was also ideal, as long as Matthew made the consistency sloppy enough. Fraser had explained that he had worked in Glasgow, where he had given thiamine to all the intravenous drug users.

'Well, thank you!' I had muttered under my breath. 'Let's just make this clear, I am not anorexic, I don't abuse drugs and I am not an alcoholic, so why would I be deficient in thiamine?'

Fraser could be blunt to the point of rudeness. He was an excellent doctor, but sometimes his frankness was not welcome.

That night I looked into the thiamine content of different foods, and found that it was present in almost everything. Nuts and seeds contain thiamine in abundance. Along with the soups and smoothies, I also ate nuts, sunflower seeds and pumpkin seeds. These were an easy snack to provide me with energy whilst I worked. I couldn't possibly be thiamine deficient. In fact, Fraser had to agree that of the two of us, my diet was far healthier and contained more thiamine than his.

Feeling rather smug in the knowledge that I had the healthier, thiamine-enhanced diet, the subject was dropped.

Some months later, while reading more papers about my symptoms, I discovered an article featuring beriberi – a condition seen in poor countries due to thiamine deficiency. I was astounded to realise that I had the classic symptoms.

I was fascinated by the discovery. Although it was not identified as thiamine deficiency until the late nineteenth century, Jacobus Bontius first observed the signs in sufferers in the West Indies, and he then described the condition.[6] In the early 16th century, he wrote:

'De Paralyseos quadam specie . . .

Affectus quidam admodum molestus, hic homines infestat, qui ab incolis Beriberi (quod ovum sonat) vocatur. Credo quia quos malum istud invasit nictando genibus, ac elevando crura, tanquam ovis ingrediantur. Estque species Paralyseos seu potius Tremoris: Nam motum, sensumque manum, ac pedum, immo vero aliquando totius corporis depravat, ac tremere facit.'

Translated:

'A type of paralysis . . .

A certain very troublesome state, these people are disturbed by a condition, which the inhabitants call beriberi (which sounds like sheep). I believe because this illness invades and weakens the knees, it causes people to elevate their legs, walking like sheep. It is a type of paralysis, or rather tremor: disrupting the motion and sensation of the hands and feet, indeed sometimes the whole body is affected causing shaking.'

More recent descriptions of the symptoms of beriberi confirmed that weight loss, emotional disturbance, impaired sensory perception, weakness and pain in the limbs and periods of irregular heart rate were typical. One translation for the word 'beriberi' was 'sheep', other translations were 'weakness' and 'I can't, I can't', in Sinhalese. I had gradually developed all the symptoms. I read more. The large sensory nerves were affected, including the sensory nerves that give information to the brain on position sense, so-called proprioception. The motor fibres were often spared. The patient would often present with ataxia, a loss of balance and coordination.

Loss of sensation. Loss of balance. Lack of coordination. This is why I was unsteady when I walked in the dark, why I couldn't tell where my feet were in the car, and why I often lost my balance and fell. *The falls!* It all made sense. I felt oddly relieved that I had at last found out what the problem was.

I also read about thiamine in several books on vitamins. Thiamine deficiency also caused 'burning feet syndrome'; it was the first symptom patients experienced when they developed a peripheral neuropathy. I had also experienced this, although the first symptom I suffered was the excruciatingly sharp pains in my feet and hands. Lhermitte's sign is the electric shock-like sensation that goes down the back and into the limbs described mainly by multiple sclerosis sufferers on bending the neck; these patients have nerve damage in the spinal cord. I had this shock-like pain in my feet, hands and then in my forearms and calves. The pain only occurred if the nerve had been stretched. In this respect it was like the damaged nerves in multiple sclerosis – the shooting pains that occurred on bending, or rather stretching, the spinal cord. I had nerve damage to the peripheral, sensory nerves.

I needed no other confirmation. I telephoned Fraser the next morning.

'Hou's it gaun?' he asked, sounding non-committal.

'You were right!' I exclaimed, unable to keep the excitement out of my voice. I was so keen to tell him about my discovery that I had forgotten he would be in the middle of a ward round.

'Richt 'bout whit?' he enquired, sounding unusually polite. It was not often I told him he was right about something.

'Thiamine, I must be thiamine deficient. It's what is causing the pains. It's neuralgia, not arthralgia!' I blurted it all out, eager for him to understand my desperation.

'Can a gie ye Pabrinex?'

He was offering to treat me with a solution of high-dose intravenous vitamins, which contain thiamine. I was touched by his immediate, kind response.

I dressed quickly, drove to the hospital and walked along the corridor to my old unit, avoiding glances and trying to stay upright so as not to embarrass myself. I sat in an armchair in his office, whilst he registered me as a patient and collected the paraphernalia required for cannulation and an infusion. As he wheeled in the drip stand, he chatted to me in his usual jovial, good-humoured manner. He told me that it wasn't too much trouble and that it was worth trying. He said he believed I had the symptoms and that he was prepared to try what was effectively experimental treatment.

It was his turn to be smug. 'Ah told ye! Ye'd lost aw yer weight, ye must be,' he said, mocking me gently, as the needle punctured my skin.

'Quich shag!' he said.

I was surprised at his remark. He smiled reassuringly at me whilst advancing the cannula up the vessel. I had clearly misheard him. Fraser and I had been colleagues for 10 years and had become close friends. We had worked together on the unit and arranged educational meetings together. No, this wasn't a proposition. In all respects it was totally out of context and out of character. I knew that Fraser was happily married and very principled.

A quick jag! Ah! He was telling me I should expect pain from the needle. I smiled to myself. He obviously used this expression regularly. I wondered how many of his patients had also misheard. Perhaps, though, they weren't cloth heads like me. Over the years, Fraser and I had been to conferences together and I recalled one in Edinburgh a couple of years earlier. He had told me a true story about a medic who lived in Queen Street, who, in 1847, had entertained his guests with chloroform after dinner. This dalliance had resulted in the discovery of the first anaesthetic agent.

The blood flushed back into the cannula in my forearm. Fortunately, the only parts of my body that hadn't shrunk were my veins, which were still like the major branches of a tree. The liquid had a characteristic strong, earthy, sulphur scent that overcame even my poor sense of smell. The infusion bag was connected to a long plastic tube with a clamp, which, when opened, allowed the liquid to slowly fill the line. The line was connected to the cannula and I sat and waited, expecting to be able to report back on the success or otherwise of the experiment after a few days. I felt the coldness of the fluid track up my arm and then I started to feel a little flushed. I initially thought it was just excitement, but then I realised that flushing was a side effect, particularly if the infusion rate was too high.

After 20 minutes, the bright amber liquid had almost completely run through the line and the infusion bag was empty. I felt a wave of calm pass over me. My entire body felt relaxed and it was as though every cell was smiling. The relief was dramatic. I actually felt human again. The fog in my brain had lifted and I felt like a totally different person from the one who had staggered into the unit just 30 minutes earlier. After approximately another half an hour, my hands gradually improved and an hour later even the pains in my feet had disappeared.

It was bizarre – I was cured! If I had been a religious person, I would have been praising the Lord. This was a miracle. I thanked Fraser profusely and almost skipped out of the unit to get on with the rest of my life. I had so many things I needed to do and now I had the energy to do them. It was incredible.

I phoned Matthew to let him know that I was better. I don't think he'd totally accepted that I had felt ill and so it was difficult for him to respond positively to the amazing news. That afternoon, I walked around the town and did the shopping, picked up the children from school and then returned home to do the ironing and housework. The children were happy to see me acting more normally. It was great to be more involved with them, rather than feeling that everything was such an effort and being bad tempered and disengaged. I'm sure they noticed the difference, but they accepted the cure without much ado. That night I slept amazingly well. I felt a little fatigued the next day, but still had no pain in my hands or feet. I felt certain that I must be better.

I worked out that I had developed a sensory neuropathy (impairment of the nerves involved with sensation), with severe neuropathic pains and a glove-and-stocking loss of sensation. I may also have had an encephalopathy (confusion and memory disturbance commonly seen in alcoholics with thiamine deficiency). These problems had been resolved by the high-dose of thiamine. I immediately bought some Vitamin B1 tablets and started taking a large number of them. I had to swallow them whole, and they tasted revolting.

I woke the following day, 48 hours after having the infusion, feeling that I must have dreamt the last two days. It was as if my treatment with Fraser had never happened. I was exhausted, having woken again in the middle of the night with the palpitations. I felt like crying. I had the restless legs and the pains in my hands and feet again. The disappointment was devastating. I had been on a high, as though I had been on a rollercoaster ride, but now I was stuck at the bottom of a dip. In desperation I phoned Fraser again and explained my predicament. With the same good nature he administered another intravenous infusion of the intense yellow liquid and I experienced the same incredible response as I had the first time. Reluctantly, I agreed not to go crazy this time. Again, just 48-hours later, the pain returned. Each subsequent infusion gave me relief for two days only. It was completely inexplicable. In my bid to get better, I was bruised from the cannula sites and hooked on intravenous vitamins.

Oral thiamine simply didn't work. I even tried placing it sublingually (under the tongue), but it just tasted awful and didn't make any difference. The thiamine placed next to my gums just made my teeth jingle and feel hypersensitive, as though I had brushed them with sandpaper infused with acid.

I once again resorted to the electronic library, reading everything there was to know about thiamine. I certainly felt more mentally alert now and had a sense of purpose and real drive, a determination to unravel this heinous malady. I felt like a spy put in charge of uncovering a major plot against a few vulnerable people who had been afflicted with malrotation of the intestines. I learnt about the discovery of thiamine in prisoners and that thiamine deficiency was also a problem on ships in the 19th century, when low-ranking sailors were fed a rice-based diet and little else. As it occurred in outbreaks, it was originally thought to be an infectious disease.

Thiamine was the first of the essential nutrients to be discovered in 1912 by the Polish biochemist Casimir Funk, who called it 'Anti-Beriberi Factor'. These types of nutrients were called vital amines, or vitamines for short. The name vitamine indicated that they contained a chemical compound known as an amino group (nitrogen and hydrogen atoms), and that they were essential for life. Thiamine was named aneurin at first. This was short for antineuritic vitamin, highlighting the effect it had on the nervous system.

I looked up anti-thiamine factors in foods and read about sulphites; these thiamine-destroying compounds are commonly used as preservatives. There were anti-thiamine compounds in coffee, too, but since I could find no clear, technical explanation for this I began to veer away from the non-scientific websites. I had drunk moderate amounts of coffee in the past, but was this really enough to cause thiamine deficiency? It seemed very unlikely, otherwise most doctors would be ill like me.

I discovered that alcohol consumption also reduces thiamine absorption. It seemed that the cellular thiamine-transporter proteins in the wall of the intestines are affected by it, and so the thiamine can't be absorbed. I wondered whether this was why I always felt so much worse after drinking: the insomnia was made worse, and I always became shaky.

I caused myself yet more anxiety when I discovered that mercury poisoning was a potential problem. There were a large number of pseudoscience reports highlighting that the ingestion of mercury could be the cause of a number of neurodegenerative conditions. There were also scientific reports claiming that acute mercury poisoning causes shakes, emotional lability, insomnia, muscle twitching, weakness, sensory disturbance . . . in fact, all the symptoms I had experienced, which were also identical to the ones that come with beriberi. When I was a teenager, I had an amalgam root filling, which would have been 50% mercury, drilled into my facial bone. This had now leached out into my gum, leaving an unpleasant black stain. Could I really have mercury poisoning? There seemed little convincing evidence. Amalgam fillings were deemed safe, but nevertheless phasing them out had been recommended. I wondered whether they were safe in normal individuals, but caused problems in low thiamine states. Perhaps it was another contributory factor. What I really needed to know was how I could have become thiamine deficient.

I wondered how I could have been so wrong about the pains and tried to remember the symptoms. Although I described them as joint pains, it was actually the bending of the joint that hurt. Each time I picked up a mug an excruciatingly sharp, lancinating pain shot up my arm. I should have realised that it wasn't arthritis, as the joints were never tender, swollen, or red. Initially the pains had been intermittent, only occurring if the nerve had been stretched. By the time I was experiencing constant burning pains in my hands and feet, I had also developed a loss of sensation, fasciculations and pains in my calves, and so the diagnosis of neuropathy was more obvious.

If I had been mistaken into thinking that the pains experienced on moving my joints, and the pains felt in the small joints of my feet and wrists were due to arthritis, how many other doctors had been duped? After all, arthritis due to 'wear and tear' was now so common.

How many patients, like me, had been the victims of misdiagnosis?

Seesaws

1990

AS A MEDICAL STUDENT, I worked in the labs with a now celebrated liver fibrosis researcher. He is famous in the liver world, which comprises a relatively small network of like-minded people. Until that time it was understood that liver scarring (fibrosis and cirrhosis) was due to an excess amount of the scar protein, collagen. My colleague was working on a slightly different theory, challenging this accepted belief. He was trying to prove – with some success – that the underlying problem wasn't that too much collagen was produced, rather that the cause of scarring was because the collagen wasn't being broken down. Therefore, liver cirrhosis or fibrosis occurs when the protease enzymes (chemicals in the body that facilitate the breakdown of proteins) don't work as well. Collagen is thus allowed to accumulate unchallenged, because of a deficiency in the enzyme that controls it.

I was working in the same laboratory, however, I was conducting research on pancreatic tissue for a scientist rather than a physician. Although I would rather have been studying the liver, it made no difference, as I was really only learning the basics. The scientists' group, which included me, was investigating the role of a regenerating gene. To try and promote this gene, I was culturing cells in special nutrient broth and feeding them chemicals and nutrients in different concentrations. The whole process, from taking the pancreatic cells, keeping the cells alive and then extracting the genetic material, took seven days. I basically had no days off. It wasn't as arduous as working on the wards, but there were different pressures, namely getting the experiment to work! Each step had to be carried out meticulously: the cells were prone to infections and sometimes refused to grow, the chemicals were often too toxic and enzymes destroyed the genes. These enzymes were apparently everywhere, like spies in the lab. I had to protect my cells – my hard work. One of the steps involved gently warming them using a water bath. But one day I got distracted and somehow failed to notice that the water bath had been set to a much higher temperature. I had basically cooked my cells and I didn't know what to do. My week's work was slowly steaming in front of me. In a spur-of-the-moment decision, I decided to analyse the cells anyway. It wouldn't work, but I could do with the practice, as my experimental technique was unreliable. Surely practice would help perfect it.

The hypothesis I was working on was that cells and tissues are capable of repairing, regrowing and even regenerating. I didn't really believe it at the time, as it was fairly clear that there were some diseases, such as heart failure, liver cirrhosis and dementia, where the damage was done; once you had heart failure, for example, there didn't seem to be any chance of recovery and treatments were prescribed to control symptoms only. The overarching hypothesis was explained using a seesaw diagram, and in healthy tissue this was balanced. On one side of the seesaw was 'injury' and on the other was 'repair'. If the damage from toxins, such as alcohol or viruses, increased out of proportion to the regenerative mechanisms, then the net result was disease, which could be avoided if repair and regeneration predominated and injury was controlled.

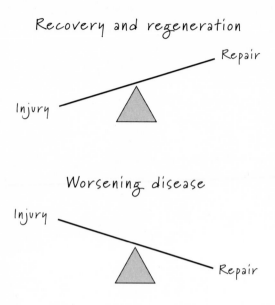

Incredibly, boiling my cells promoted the regenerating gene and suddenly I had another hypothesis. This gene produced a 'heat shock protein' in response to stress or heat, and the protein seemed to have a range of functions in the body. I was excited by this revelation. I read all the journal articles I could find about this new protein and its uses, as our gene was rebranded. Heat shock proteins, also termed 'molecular chaperones', are produced to protect the proteins in the cells from denaturing. My supervisor thought it was a specific heat shock protein – 'hsp70' – that was being produced when I had inadvertently cooked my cells. It may not have been a life-changing event, but for me it felt terribly important. I was thrilled to think I had made a discovery, even if it was mainly down to serendipity, or rather stupidity!

Despite my initial scepticism, I enjoyed the camaraderie in the lab. I had learnt new techniques, original science and improved my ability to think through problems – skills that at the time I didn't fully appreciate.

★

I was interested in liver disease, especially alcoholic and non-alcoholic liver disease. What intrigued me was why only a small proportion of heavy drinkers develop cirrhosis. Also, why do only a fraction of obese patients develop significant non-alcoholic fatty liver disease? In both these conditions, if you looked at a section of liver under a microscope, there was fat accumulation and inflammation – the histology of both conditions was remarkably similar. Why was that? There had to be another, as yet unrecognised factor.

I recalled a particularly young patient who presented with jaundice, deranged liver function and nosebleeds. It was not clear why he was jaundiced. He had all the blood tests to ascertain a cause, and as he worked outside he was also tested for Weil's disease or Leptospirosis, which is contracted from infectious rat urine. All his tests were negative. He had markedly deranged clotting, which precluded a liver biopsy. We were flummoxed. We sought a further history of possible alcohol intake from his family. He worked closely with his father and his parents were adamant that he didn't drink. Each morning, the patient and his father took a packed lunch to work, with the patient also taking a high-energy sports drink, as it was physical work.

Tragically, the patient continued to deteriorate and despite our efforts, he bled to death on the ward. He was only 24. He had suffered a massive variceal bleed. Varices are the dilated veins at the bottom of the oesophagus, which can develop in liver disease as a result of increased pressure in the liver and a diversion in the circulation to vessels not equipped to handle the blood volume. Rather like a road closure diverting traffic along small, inadequate routes, causing a car crash on the country lanes. Shortly before his death, his parents were able to discover the cause of his liver disease. The high-energy drink bottles contained whisky and lemonade. Presumably he had been refilling the bottles with a cocktail that sadly proved to be fatal.

I'm not sure exactly what attracted me to this specialty, where there were often terrible consequences like the one just described. I did enjoy questioning the accepted theories of disease processes and partly regretted not having pursued an academic career. The time to apply for research grants clashed with having children, and my 'pregnancy brain' did not impress the grant officers. I had tried a few times to get a research position but had been unsuccessful.

'If you have any more children, you can forget becoming a consultant,' my supervising consultant told me after I returned to work following the birth of my second child. Despite the 'advice', and having four children, I had become a consultant, but the grant always eluded me. Had I succeeded, I would have investigated a condition known as syndrome X, but I would have remained largely clinical, seeing patients rather than working in a laboratory on an animal model of the disease. Syndrome X, also known as the metabolic syndrome, has intrigued doctors for decades. Despite its increasing prevalence and the fact that it is easy to recognise (the diverse symptoms include high blood pressure, high blood sugar, large waist and high cholesterol), there is still no universal explanation. Patients often have a poor prognosis, dying of heart disease or strokes, despite the fact there is often very little wrong with their major vessels.

I can still visualise the ward round in Southampton with the team, when the registrar and senior registrar were discussing a case. It was then that I came across the new terminology – 'non-alcoholic fatty liver disease' (NAFLD); this was syndrome X affecting the liver.

Syndrome X, or metabolic syndrome, was a medical mystery, a puzzle, and as medicine subdivided further into subspecialties, each specialist recognised a part of the syndrome with unique significance to their specialty, but with little understanding of the effect on other organs or systems in the body. Syndrome X was the unexplained association between heart disease, high cholesterol, high blood pressure and poor outcome. These patients did not do well with treatments to open up the major blood supply to the heart. They did not respond to 'thrombolysis' (using a drug to dissolve a clot) or to 'angioplasty' (using a balloon on a catheter to mechanically open up the arteries). This was because the large vessels were not the problem; the problem was the smaller blood vessels, the so-called microvascular. There were obvious signs of damage to the small vessels, and with no discernible cause, the question was why?

Puzzles

2011

WHITE AND GREEN WATER LILIES floating on a lake in front of a country estate; grey, wrinkled elephants in the dusty, khaki grassland; emperor penguins huddled together in the freezing Antarctic; shimmering goldfish swimming amongst a coral reef …

I had always enjoyed doing jigsaw puzzles. I liked quietly studying the contours and colours, sorting out the pieces into sky blue, grey ice, brown savanna. The satisfaction of adding another chink to the whole picture gives a real sense of achievement.

The jigsaw on the table in front of me depicted an old street in a market town; the buildings, with their sandstone walls and gated entrances, resembled the Latin Quarter in Paris or the old part of Villeneuve-lès-Avignon. Only it wasn't Paris or Provence, as there was a red postbox in the wall of a townhouse. The houses nearest to the junction and in the forefront had white lace curtains at the windows. The pieces with whitewashed, cracked walls and shadows cast by wiring had to be separated from the window pieces. The left-hand side was in a darker shade and there were few clues to help connect them to the edge pieces. The right-hand side was not dissimilar in colour, although a street lamp and guttering provided some landmarks.

When I placed pieces together erroneously, I had to move

around sections of the edge. These pieces initially looked as if they fitted, but as I completed more of the puzzle it was clear I had been misled.

Sitting quietly like this and not rushing around was part of my recuperation. I was able to maintain my weight, and with thrice-weekly thiamine injections my other symptoms were under control. Even so, the jigsaw I was now unscrambling in my mind had thousands of pieces. I'd slotted together a few of them in one corner and a few more opposite that, but the middle was still missing, with the key pieces yet to be identified.

The most important piece of the puzzle came to me whilst I reflected on a family holiday in the Lake District with friends the previous year. It wasn't the actual holiday that was causing me to reminisce, although that had highlighted my strange eating habits; it wasn't even the lack of energy or sleep, because unlike previous holidays that had strangely improved during the course of the week. Rather it was the journey there. We took two cars, mainly so that Matthew could take the bikes in his car and Emily could take her piano in mine. Aged 13, Emily was adamant that she had to practise. She couldn't possibly consider a whole week away from her piano – it was simply too much to conceive! A quick search of the local towns and villages was disappointing. There was no piano shop in Pooley Bridge, the nearest settlement to the cottage, and no bars that had pianos – not that this would have been an ideal solution! The only feasible option was to dismantle the Clavinova and take it with us.

Irritatingly, in the few days before the trip, I succumbed to a gum infection and started a course of antibiotics. I couldn't remember the last time I had required antibiotics. It was over a year since I had needed them for a chest infection. I started the drive with the usual shooting pains in my wrists and discomfort in my feet. We convened in a service station on the way north and I remarked that the pains in my hands had begun to improve. I showed them to everyone, rubbing them together joyfully. I was so glad to be pain free.

Unfortunately, shortly after our return home, I developed the pains again. Naturally, Matthew assumed that the relief of being on holiday had been the sole reason for the improvement in my health, even though it had actually been more stressful for me and had required more exertion. The return of my symptoms confirmed his opinion that stress was at the root of all my problems. Whereas the only factor that had changed was that I had taken a course of antibiotics. Why was this?

*

Finally, recognising that the only abnormal finding on the tests was the malrotation, I was referred to a surgeon, who also happened to be a colleague and friend of many years. Coincidentally, he had been on the holiday with us in the Lake District. The surgeon practised in another hospital and, as the bowel surgery required was unusual for someone of my age (it's usually diagnosed in childhood), he consulted a paediatric surgeon, who was more familiar with the corrective surgical procedure. Aged 42, I was deemed too old for the children's services.

The surgeon took a thorough history and made a detailed record of all my abdominal symptoms. I was worried, as he had initially seemed indifferent. This case was outside his area of expertise and I felt certain that he too would dismiss it and that I would be left stumbling in the dark again. I had almost given up hope when, a few days later, he contacted me to say that not having encountered this problem before he had read up on cases similar to mine. He sent me copies of these from the literature. The pattern of abdominal pains, obstructive symptoms and reflux had been described in patients with malrotation, recurrent volvulus and Ladd's bands (scar tissue forming adhesions internally). Of course, I had already worked this out. I had also read similar papers, but the relief I felt was overwhelming. I burst into tears of happiness. Finally someone believed me. At last there was a glimmer of hope.

The surgeon explained that classically patients with this condition present in the first year of life. I wanted to tell him that I had presented in the first few hours, but that the doctors hadn't believed my mother, but I decided bitterness was not going to help. I knew that the 'classical description' was unhelpful, as, in my experience, patients don't quote from the textbooks. The surgeon said he had come across a series of cases where people had presented at various stages of adulthood.

The surgeon was, like me, concerned about my nutritional status. He had the benefit of having known me for many years and he recognised the profound loss of weight and muscle mass was abnormal. He referred me to another gastroenterologist in his hospital. This was the one who questioned me about my tremor. He agreed that I was malnourished and requested a vitamin D-level test. It was whilst waiting for the result of this that I started the high-dose vitamin infusions after realising I had beriberi. The vitamin D result was delayed.

I was engrossed in the thiamine literature, trying to understand why I was thiamine deficient despite taking a thiamine-rich diet. I was also baffled by the fact that intravenous thiamine relieved the symptoms. Antibiotics had also seemed to help during the Lake District trip, but oral thiamine was useless.

★

I forgot about the vitamin D-level test until weeks later, when the gastroenterologist telephoned to tell me it showed severe deficiency. The level was 4 ng/ml. Deficiency occurs with a level less than 30 ng/ml and less than 10 ng/ml is severely deficient. If only this had been checked months or years ago it would have signified organic rather than psychosomatic illness. I was treated with repeated intramuscular injections of high-dose vitamin D, as well as the intravenous B vitamins, becoming a human pincushion just as the sensation in my skin was also beginning to recover!

The vitamin D level, as it was so abnormal, triggered a dramatic change in attitude and a series of investigations were rapidly arranged. A CT scan showed a 'possibly bulky uncinate process'. In other words, part of my pancreas appeared abnormal. I had an endoscopic ultrasound to investigate further. This involved swallowing a large ultrasound probe on the end of a flexible light source. Hence I had to be heavily sedated, which I disliked. The indications for each test were never fully discussed with me. I assumed they were looking for a double pancreatic duct (pancreatic divisum), which can be associated with malrotation, but I wasn't sure.

'It's OK,' the consultant performing the endoscopy said, rather informally, once I had recovered sufficiently from the sedation.

I had a barium follow through, arranged at short notice. It was clear that strings were being pulled, and colleagues were seeing me outside their regular working hours, for which I was grateful. However, I had the impression that they were trying to protect me and I didn't feel informed. I also thought it was extremely unlikely that it would lead to a diagnosis. I realised that it was important to cover all bases; after all, I was a medical enigma. During the barium follow through I had to wait for the viscous liquid to pass into my small intestines before more images could be taken. Matthew and I passed the time in an empty waiting room in the radiology department, which was basically a couple of chairs in a basement corridor.

'I wonder why they are doing this? Why all the urgency?' Matthew said.

'They are looking for small bowel lymphoma,' I replied knowingly. I had already worked out that the weight loss with severe malabsorption pointed to disease in the part of the gut responsible for absorption. I had normal liver function and a normal pancreas, which left the small intestines. There were a few disease processes that affected the small intestines, such as coeliac disease, and most of these I was sure had already been ruled out. A couple of years previously, Matthew's godmother had died of small bowel lymphoma. It was possible, but highly unlikely. Eventually I was told that there was no lymphoma; I didn't have cancer.

On the way home in the car, Matthew told me that the radiologist, who happened to be a friend of a friend, had explained to him that they were looking for small bowel lymphoma. He hadn't really believed me earlier when I'd told him that, and he seemed to be imparting this as fresh news. He appeared to be deaf when it came to bad news. But now this form of cancer had been excluded, he was able to discuss it. I remember feeling irritated that the radiologist hadn't thought to tell me. I was being cushioned from potentially bad news – wrapped in cotton wool – but there was clearly something wrong with me and I wanted to be involved in finding out what that was.

It was at this stage that I started to think more laterally about how this could all fit together. After starting the thiamine treatment, I was able to think more clearly and logically and I spent hours working out the events that had led to my current state.

I had thiamine deficiency – there was no doubt in my mind about that. Despite the lack of an available test, my response to treatment was undeniable. I also had severe vitamin D deficiency. I was beginning to recognise a pattern. It is well known that Vitamin D is malabsorbed when there are bacteria in the small intestines . . .

I wanted to know if thiamine was ever 'malabsorbed'. Could bacteria destroy it, too?

Reflecting on the past two years, my symptoms deteriorated when I stopped aspirating. Until then I had been taking regular courses of antibiotics for the chest infections. The same process that had damaged my other nerves had presumably also affected the muscles keeping my bowels moving.

My poor night vision was probably due to vitamin A deficiency, which is often associated with vitamin D deficiency, as they are both fat-soluble vitamins. But what causes poor absorption of fat and, consequently, fat-soluble vitamins?

The neuropathic pains in my hands had improved while taking antibiotics while on holiday in the Lake District.

This *had* to be the link.

Dredging my memory, I had come across 'bacterial overgrowth' in a specific group of patients. As the name suggests, bacterial overgrowth, or small intestinal bacterial overgrowth, is the presence of excessive bacteria in the small intestines. This can lead to poor absorption of fat-soluble vitamins, such as vitamin D. In the cases I recalled, bacterial overgrowth was associated with liver disease: fatty liver in particular. These patients had a stagnant loop of bowel as a result of early bariatric or weight-loss surgery. There was a similar association in patients who had almost total removal of the small bowel and were reliant on complete parenteral nutrition. Once again, there was a lack of gut movement and so the contents of the gut were static, like a blocked drain.

The surgical procedure commonly performed for morbid obesity in the 1960s was a jejunal-ileal bypass. This involved bypassing most of the small bowel, leaving it as a blind-ending, 'stagnant' loop – the blind loop of bowel connected with the distal end of the small intestines. As a result of having this surgery, patients developed joint pains, muscle pains and skin disorders. It was called arthritis-dermatitis syndrome. I was taught that the inflammatory changes leading to arthritis-dermatitis were due to immune complexes circulating. At that time, these immune complexes were the trendy explanation for anything that was not well understood.

Searching for cases online, I found three reports of immune complexes after jejunal-ileal bypass. In one there was no correlation with the development of arthritis[7], but a further article suggested there might be a connection, with higher levels of immune reaction in patients with arthritis.[8] Interestingly, the third paper reported on a patient with clear vasculitis and acute renal failure who had developed definite immune complex disease against an identifiable bacterial antigen.[9] I wondered whether these people actually had neuropathy. It was possible that the 'joint pains' they suffered weren't due to any process in the joint but because of nerve damage, and that the stretching of the nerve fibres upon bending a joint caused the pain. The arthritis was always described as 'non-destructive', so there was no evidence of erosions or damage to the joint surface. The skin lesions were described as papules (small bumps in the skin) and blisters, with panniculitis (skin infection).

Another team of researchers investigated the effect of self-filling blind loops in a rat model, showing that bacterial overgrowth in the loops slowed down the small-intestinal muscle and nerve activity, but that antibiotics or surgical removal of the blind loops corrected the problem. They concluded that the reduced gut motility was due to the bacteria flora.[10] It seemed that the bacteria were actually producing something that was having an effect on the nerve supply to the gut. They had made the connection between bacteria, antibiotics and nerve dysfunction, albeit in rats.

In my case, each time I suffered with volvulus (twisted guts) there would be inflammation on the serosal membrane (the outer surface) of my gut. This would heal but in the process formed scars. In the medical profession, this scar tissue is known as Ladd's bands. These are adhesions between the normally slippery, shiny serosal surfaces. The Ladd's bands caused small bowel obstruction and stagnant guts. I felt sure there was an association between my obstructed guts and the thiamine deficiency I had developed. Antibiotics had helped. Did I have bacteria in my small intestines?

I searched for a connection between thiamine and jejunal-ileal bypass, finding three articles. There was one case report of a reversible peripheral neuropathy due to thiamine deficiency – 'atrophic beriberi' – in a patient who had a poor diet.[11] Another one described three new complications of jejunal-ileal bypass: acute colonic dilatation, beriberi and lupus eythematosus (an autoimmune condition).[12] The final one was a review, which happened to mention thiamine along with every other vitamin.[13] No one else had made the connection between nerve damage, thiamine deficiency and bacteria.

The patients with jejunal-ileal bypass surgery not only developed fat in their liver, but this occasionally progressed to advanced liver disease. This is similar to fatty liver disease or syndrome X, in that a proportion of individuals will develop fibrosis (scarring) in the liver. This was the link to the area of medicine that had always fascinated me – the metabolic syndrome.

There was one particular paper that I read and reread, and enthusiastically reported on to Matthew over porridge the following morning. A researcher called Lakhani[14] disputed the widely held belief that thiamine deficiency following bariatric surgery was due to postoperative vomiting. He hypothesised that it was because of small intestinal bacterial overgrowth. He followed up patients who had undergone Roux-en-Y gastric bypass surgery. This is a procedure that drastically reduces the stomach capacity, emptying the stomach into the distal small intestine and reducing the absorptive area for nutrients.

Lakhani reported on two studies performed retrospectively. In the first, 49% of the patients were found to be thiamine deficient after the bariatric surgery. 72% of those who were thiamine deficient were also found to have elevated folate levels. Folate is another B vitamin – vitamin B9, which is essential for health as it is used in making red blood cells. It is also recommended for pregnant women to reduce spina bifida, a congenital deformity of the spine. Lakhani stated that a high folate level was a marker of small intestinal bacterial overgrowth. The small bowel bacteria synthesise folate, which is then readily absorbed leading to measurable increases in human blood folate levels.

The second study was really exciting. The patients with low thiamine levels had glucose hydrogen breath tests, which turned out to be positive, confirming the presence of bacteria in the small intestine. Then they were given oral thiamine and their levels were rechecked. They hadn't changed – they were not able to absorb thiamine. A group of these patients received oral antibiotics and in all of them the thiamine levels returned to normal.

This study proved that thiamine deficiency was treatable with antibiotics, just as it had been in my case. Presumably, this was due to the presence of bacteria in the small intestines. Somehow, bacterial overgrowth was leading to thiamine deficiency. After the Roux-en-Y gastric bypass surgery, these patients were left with a section of gut that wouldn't clear completely; the bypassed remnant of stomach and the adjacent part of the proximal small intestines formed a blind-ending, stagnant loop of bowel.

Bacterial overgrowth → Thiamine deficiency

I worked out that not only was I thiamine deficient and the treatment with intravenous thiamine had been successful, but also that antibiotic treatment was effective. I was now certain that my condition had deteriorated when I stopped needing regular courses of antibiotics for repeated chest infections. Lakhani had also realised the link between bacteria in the small intestine and thiamine deficiency.

Out of curiosity, I looked up my folate level. It was very high, significantly higher than the upper limit of normal. It was reported as >40 ug/L, when the upper limit of normal is 15 ug/L. It was odd because as a physician, I had never worried about someone having too high a folate; I wasn't aware of any diseases being associated with it. Besides, a high folate wouldn't register as abnormal – in fact, the lab would have reported it as normal. Abnormal results are helpfully highlighted in some way, either in bold or with asterisks, but a high folate wouldn't have drawn attention – only a low one would be deemed a cause for concern.

Lakhani also reported that some patients had a high folate with a normal thiamine level. I wondered whether these patients would develop thiamine deficiency in due course.

I had bacterial overgrowth. I had thiamine deficiency. It all made perfect sense. I had an answer.

I was now reading papers on small intestinal bacterial overgrowth.[15] It seemed that bacterial overgrowth was increasingly being recognised as quite common. As well as the postsurgical guts, I learnt that there were other factors that contributed to bacterial overgrowth, including repeated courses of antibiotics, immunodeficiency and even organ failure; for example, liver cirrhosis, chronic pancreatitis and renal failure.

★

After this incredible discovery, I tried to explain my hypothesis to my colleague, Richard, who worked in a nearby research institute. I rated his opinion. He was one of the kindest doctors I knew and he always had time for his patients. But our conversation didn't quite go as I'd hoped.

'What do you want, a Nobel Prize?' he sniggered.

The sarcasm was caustic, and I couldn't stop myself from repeating his words over and over. I had been so excited about sharing my revelation with someone I considered a friend, someone I respected.

'So, you have a study of n=1,' he had pointed out.

He was right. I had only one person in this experiment – me. It wasn't possible to randomise one person, so it could all be a placebo effect. There had been a crossover, when treatment had been stopped and restarted. I knew it wouldn't help to say that I had read online forums and that there were other patients suffering just like me – no one was helping them, either. I had mentioned my idea for a proper trial – explaining that no one else had made the connection. I was convinced I was right and potentially onto something important. I desperately hoped it would help others, as well as help me.

'He made me sound nuts!' I later fumed to my husband. 'He didn't even listen to me, he just sat there laughing and smirking!'

Richard's response was particularly hurtful, as over the years we had often discussed a mutual interest in non-alcoholic fatty liver disease, sharing an enthusiasm to see an effective treatment. At present there really was none, other than to advise the patient to lose weight, which was often ineffective. My idea was to run a trial in patients with non-alcoholic fatty liver disease – metabolic syndrome of the liver. I now felt certain it was treatable with antibiotics and thiamine supplementation. I knew I didn't have all the answers, but I also knew I was onto something potentially quite important. Why couldn't Richard see that?

Unlike with my jigsaw puzzle, there was no point in even attempting the edges. There seemed no edge to this puzzle; it was assuming a larger and larger area, becoming ever more uncontainable. This was a jigsaw of as yet uncountable pieces. My discoveries were initially written in diaries and subsequently collated into Word documents and filed under the relevant heading. I was expanding my knowledge of the field daily. Every night I would search for more information on thiamine, bacterial overgrowth, gastric bypass surgery and the metabolic syndrome. Each piece of information slotted somewhere on the board. Slowly, with this knowledge, the unexplainable was becoming explicable. Completing this puzzle was giving me a sense of worth, as well as a tremendous feeling of hope.

Red Rice

THIAMINE WAS THE FIRST vitamin to be discovered, but its presence was known about long before its chemical structure was revealed. Adolphe Vorderman, a Dutch prison medical officer, who worked in the East Indies in the mid to late 19th century, made the connection that beriberi often occurred in prisoners after feeding them different coloured rice.[16] The prisoners fed red rice complete with the outer crimson shell had a much lower incidence than the ones fed white rice. I read that beriberi reached epidemic proportions as a result of a change in the practice of preparing rice.[17] With mechanisation, rice milling became fashionable. Milling peels the bran (husk) off the grain and then polishing the rice produces the shiny, white appearance still popular today. Many people eat a diet that consists of mostly white rice.

Christian Eijkman, another Dutch physician, conducted experiments on chickens. He noted that those fed scraps of white rice developed weakness and opisthotonus (stargazing) – extension of the neck caused by spasms in the neck muscles.[18] In the experiments, the chickens fed the red rice scraps were not affected. There was a certain amount of serendipity involved with this discovery, along with astute observation and careful documentation. Feeding the affected chickens with rice husk (unmilled rice) led to an improvement in their neurological ailment. Hence, from these tests it was surmised that the rice husk contained an essential component and that a diet deficient in this vital nutrient caused beriberi. Thus, treatment with rice husk was curative.

Reading about these experiments made me think about the ducklings or chicks I'd encountered in Haarlem and at the country house; both had exhibited this stargazing posture. At the time, there had been no clear reason, but now it seemed that, like me, they had been thiamine deficient. Was this too far-fetched? It was certainly odd that both lots had suffered a devastating disease. It had to be more than a coincidence, but I didn't feel I could discuss this concern with anyone without inviting further ridicule.

Having established that thiamine deficiency was the underlying problem in beriberi, it became clear that patients suffering from this condition presented with either predominantly cardiac or predominantly neurological complications. The cardiac form was termed wet beriberi, whereas the neurological condition was known as dry beriberi. What was abundantly obvious was that the symptoms of thiamine deficiency vary widely between individuals. This makes diagnosis difficult. It is not dissimilar to cortisol deficiency in Addison's disease, where there is also an unpredictable presentation. As a result, the diagnosis is often missed. The difference is that it is relatively easy to test for cortisol deficiency, whereas apparently the test for thiamine is not overly reliable.

Instead of testing for thiamine deficiency, it is a common, accepted practice to treat patients suspected of it with thiamine supplements. The rationale for this is that these supplements are cheap, so why not? The supplements are prescribed to prevent deterioration in conditions associated with deficiency, however, there is often already irreversible damage, or damage that is extremely slow to reverse. An example of this is Korsakoff's dementia, which is a condition where patients develop a permanent loss of short-term memory. This occurs with thiamine deficiency, although it is probably also due to the effects of excess alcohol consumption combined with poor general nutrition.

I reflected on the popular myth that Columbus was the first to discover that the earth was not flat, as portrayed in navigational charts. However, this fact had actually been known about centuries beforehand, although many ancient cultures still believed in the flat Earth. The term 'Flat Earther' is applied to individuals who resolutely stick to disproven theories. It takes an incredibly long time to change entrenched beliefs.

At medical school in the late '80s, we were taught that duodenal ulcers were due to stress. Patients were prone to ulcers if they had a recognisable 'Type A' personality: highly-strung, ambitious, impatient, take-on-more-than-they-can-handle. A couple of years before this, a researcher in Australia called Barry Marshall discovered that the actual cause of duodenal ulcers was a bacterial infection. Marshall infected himself with the organism to demonstrate that it was possible for these bacteria to survive in the hostile environment of the stomach. The bacteria were subsequently named *Helicobacter pylori*. Using the new online search facility, he looked for all the papers he could find on gastric bacteria, going into the archives[19]. He was reported to have said that he felt that everyone was against him, but he knew he was right. We were still being taught the stress hypothesis in medical school lectures – the textbooks needed to be rewritten and the lecturer had to update his slides. More importantly, the science community had to believe in Marshall's hypothesis.

I thought about other paradoxes that had occurred throughout history. In northern Sweden, the land was rising as the ice cap melted and there was less weight, but for years it was thought that the sea level was falling. Likewise, Keys' 'Seven Countries Study' was controversial. Now the pendulum had swung the other way, leaving people confused about what was healthy. Was fat still bad for you?

I applied this principle to exercise. Everyone is told that it is the key to a healthy life, and I used to believe this too. I had been working on a hypothesis that by exercising our muscles we somehow detox our bodies. I realised that this simple explanation had to be flawed, because I couldn't find any scientific explanation of it. I made copious notes in the front of my diary, but the explanations never quite slotted into place. There were too many pieces missing. I thought about the exercise conundrum from a different angle. Thiamine-replete individuals have no problem exercising – Matthew was the prime example. However, people with thiamine deficiency struggle to work out and associate it with feeling worse. Any behaviour that causes deterioration tends to be avoided. Each time I exercised, I became more unwell. I felt fine whilst I was doing it, but over the following days I would become shaky and agitated. I would then struggle to sleep and usually succumb to an infection. Exercise didn't seem to benefit me. As I became less well, I also became unfit and working out became even harder. Interestingly, skiing holidays in the spring, when I was exposed to plenty of sunshine, boosted my energy levels, and presumably boosted my vitamin D level, too (vitamin D is produced in the skin in response to exposure to ultraviolet light).

Instead of exercise being something that is universally encouraged, I thought it would make more sense to question whether those who do not take it find it difficult. Perhaps, like me, it genuinely makes them feel ill. It was the Pavlovian response again. This deeply entrenched survival mode is geared to the avoidance of anything associated with discomfort. I could also understand the attraction to stuff that improves the sense of wellbeing, even if the overall result is harm.

This is the nature of dependency and addiction. Had I been addicted to sugar? I had certainly craved it, and it had temporarily improved my sense of wellbeing, although I was sure it had also somehow contributed to my condition. I wondered about the impact of certain alcoholic beverages, particularly those containing a significant amount of sugar: cider, lager, alcopops and the mixers consumed with spirits: cola and lemonade. Alcohol reduces thiamine absorption. Alcoholics are thiamine deficient. It was beginning to all make sense.

I had digressed from the thiamine searches, so I returned to the early papers and the history of the discovery. When Eijkman first travelled to the Dutch East Indies to investigate beriberi, the general consensus was that it was an infectious disease. This was because it occurred in epidemics. The cause was later found to be a dietary deficiency and the idea that beriberi might be due to an infectious agent went out of favour. However, even now beriberi continues to be a problem in many parts of the world, despite there being an ample replacement therapy. There are still outbreaks, and sometimes the cause is attributed to a poison or a heavy metal, but often this cannot be confirmed.[20] Nothing is found to be wrong. I wondered whether an infectious agent could be responsible for such cases.

Thiamine –
Essential for all Living Things

BEING GREEN FINGERED, I was aware, like many gardeners, that once a plant is damaged it seldom recovers. When I bought plants I looked for the ones with the most buds, not necessarily the tallest or biggest. I also cultivated them by taking cuttings, enjoying the thrill as tiny roots emerged from the stems. I had known for some time that plants are extremely good at protecting themselves from bacterial attack.

As I scrutinised anything thiamine related, I became absorbed in online plant biology articles. I read that thiamine is produced in the foliage and is required for root generation. Apparently, the best way to encourage root growth is to soak seeds in a thiamine-containing solution.

I wondered: *Is this what is in rooting powder?*

Simply watering plants with thiamine solution may not be effective, as microbes rapidly destroy thiamine . . .

'Again!' I wanted to shout out. I'd uncovered yet more evidence to support my hypothesis.

I reckoned botanists all over the world must be well aware of this fact . . . it was obviously no secret. I couldn't understand why no one else had made the connection. I gleaned a few essential facts from plant literature:

The important derivative of thiamine is thiamine pyrophosphate (TPP).

Thiamine with two phosphate (P) groups added.

Phosphate consists of the elements phosphorus and oxygen.

Enzymes are biological catalysts that are not used up in a reaction.

All biochemical reactions require enzymes. Chemical reactions are different to physical ones, as they result in a new compound, rather than just changing the physical state of substances. Biochemical reactions are those occurring in living (bio) things.

Coenzymes enable the enzymes to function properly.

These are substances that are essential for the enzymes to work.

TPP is a coenzyme.

So thiamine with the phosphate added is really quite important.

All living organisms rely on TPP.

All living organisms rely on thiamine. It's really important.

This all seemed straightforward, much like GCSE biology, although GCSE biology somehow misses out the important part – Thiamine or TPP.

Plants and bacteria can make thiamine.

Humans and other animals are unable to make thiamine.

Humans must take thiamine in their diet.

It is interesting that bacteria can synthesise thiamine.

The best source of thiamine is plants.

In plants, thiamine levels are increased in growing tissues, particularly seeds.

5-a-day! This is why we should eat at least five pieces of fruit or vegetables a day.

I reflected on these points. Thiamine really is vitally important for all living things. Plants use it for growth, and the parts of the plants that grow contain the most thiamine. The seeds have to support the germinating plant. This explains why nuts and seeds are rich in thiamine. I thought back to the crazy arguments I'd had with Fraser. 'I would na eat that filth!' he'd said when I'd accused him of taking my sunflower seeds.

Reading on, there were detailed accounts of the biochemical pathways involved. Substances in the body are either taken in through the diet or synthesised in biochemical reactions. A series of biochemical reactions with the necessary enzymes is usually required to make the right substances. These pathways often had multiple steps and many of the substances were involved in several pathways, with feedback loops to finely control the amounts produced.

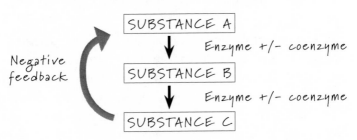

143

Clearly, if I was going to decipher research on thiamine and relate it to symptoms and medical conditions, I would need to brush up on my biochemistry. It had been 26 years since I had been exposed to biochemistry lectures at university, and I had found little reason until now to use this knowledge. If I am honest, I am not sure how much had sunk in; it hadn't seemed that relevant. Thiamine deficiency was a condition diagnosed commonly a century ago.

When I was a medical student there, Southampton University ran a relatively traditional course for the first two years. It was lecture-based and consisted of biochemistry, physiology and anatomy in the first year and sociology and psychiatry in the second. In the third year, we started the hospital attachments and were posted throughout the Wessex region. There was an elective period, allowing you to choose a country, hospital and specialty. Many people chose to go abroad and study. I travelled to South India, primarily to observe how they managed patients with leprosy, but I learnt more about the culture, people and food. The meals consisted of brown, spicy, hot liquid, served with rice and eaten with your hands. It was so hot that it made my ears ring. There was seldom any meat or vegetable matter in the dish. Unsurprisingly, I became unwell with a gastrointestinal infection and despite antibiotic treatment continued to have problems. After nine weeks of more output than input, I also lost a significant amount of weight.

At Southampton, there was an attempt to organise the training so that in the first year the anatomy of a system would be learnt at the same time as the physiology. Biochemistry was actually relevant to most organ systems and was therefore taught independently. The biochemical pathways were complex and most of them were new to me, despite studying biology at A-Level. I wished I had paid more attention and understood it better at the time. The only statement that stuck in my mind was 'Selling off the family silver.' I recall thinking at the time how teaching us about silverware was daft, but it is interesting how this is about the only part of biochemistry that I do remember. I thought that it related to the release of energy from glucose – the glycolysis pathway, but I wasn't sure of the exact biochemical processes involved.

I tried relearning these biochemical pathways, drawing them out on A4 sheets of paper and noting how all of them connected – it was like playing a giant game of Scrabble. I had to tape the pieces of paper together, but to reflect the importance of thiamine to more than one vital biochemical reaction, I needed a three-dimensional shape: a paper castle. Soon I had multiple sheets of patchwork paper pathways that were too large to fit on my desk. I resorted to strewing them across the floor, becoming spread-eagled in an unattractive posture, as though playing a complicated game of Twister – right arm to alpha-ketoglutarate, left arm to glutamate.

I relearnt that glycolysis involved the breakdown of glucose to form pyruvate. This pathway does not require oxygen, but also does not release much energy.

Glycolysis:

Glucose ⟶ Pyruvate + energy

In the absence of oxygen, glucose was then converted via pyruvate into lactate, also known as lactic acid, the substance that builds up in muscle after sprinting and causes pain.

Anaerobic metabolism (no oxygen):

Glucose ⟶ Pyruvate + energy

This was why I remembered the 'family silver'. I had been taught that if there was no oxygen, glucose was effectively 'sold cheaply' – producing very little energy. This was akin to selling the silver, or rather selling it for a lower price at a cash converter, but then having to buy it back at an inflated cost – using more energy and more oxygen. So the analogy hadn't really been about family heirlooms, but to do with pawn shops!

The next part of the metabolic pathway was the oxidation of pyruvate to acetyl coenzyme A, or acetyl CoA, and entry into the tricarboxylic acid pathway, also called the tricyclic acid or citric acid cycle (so-called as most of the chemicals are recycled). These are simply chemical reactions that occur in all organisms that undergo aerobic metabolism. In this cycle, acetyl CoA is oxidised to produce the high-energy bonds that cells can use. It takes place in the mitochondria – a specialised subcompartment of the cell – which acts like rechargeable batteries. The citric acid cycle releases the energy in food and makes it available for the organism. This was more complex to understand but, as I remembered correctly, required oxygen and produced much more energy.

Aerobic metabolism (with oxygen):

Pyruvate ⟶ Acetyl CoA → Citric acid + **ENERGY**
cycle

Pyruvate
dehydrogenase
with thiamine

What I hadn't previously appreciated was that the enzyme pyruvate dehydrogenase was essential for the oxidation of pyruvate to acetyl CoA, so that this could enter the high-energy-releasing pathway – the citric acid cycle. At medical school, I had focused on the complexity of the pathway and how many carbon atoms each chemical constituent had. It was extremely confusing but now seemed utterly useless.

I hadn't really grasped that without the first crucial step – pyruvate oxidation to form acetyl CoA – the metabolic pathway could not progress. Energy production from glucose metabolism would effectively stop at pyruvate, with little energy being produced.

Pyruvate dehydrogenase is not active in the absence of thiamine, as thiamine is an essential cofactor. Consequently, if there is no thiamine, there is poor energy release from glucose. In fact, the citric acid cycle can utilise all food sources: amino acids (from proteins), fatty acids (from fats), as well as glucose (from carbohydrates). Without thiamine, it seemed that energy release from any food source is compromised.

Pyruvate ✗➡ acetyl CoA = no energy!

Pyruvate dehydrogenase, no thiamine

Thiamine is vital in order for cells to release large amounts of energy from glucose. Without it, glucose is only partially used, and only a small amount of energy is released. The only way to release energy is to consume large amounts of glucose or sugar. This is then only partially metabolised.

Is this why I craved sugar? I asked myself.

As I worked, I read up on the latest discoveries, as well as researching historical papers. It was quite a revelation.

Thiamine is crucial.

All living things need thiamine.

Thiamine is truly an 'elixir of life'.

Thiamine is life-sustaining!

Working it through, thiamine was necessary for carbohydrate metabolism – for the breakdown of 'carbs'. Without it, the carbohydrates were not metabolised properly. This was a problem, as many people consume a lot of carbohydrates, especially since the low-fat diet has been popularised.

Thiamine is also necessary for lipid or fat metabolism. Some of the other enzymes in these pathways are also thiamine-dependent. Without thiamine, one of the by-products of fat metabolism – phytanic acid – isn't broken down properly. As a consequence, levels of phytanic acid build up. This occurs in a congenital condition called Refsum's disease, where the defective, thiamine-dependent enzyme is passed on genetically. Patients with this condition have ataxia, scaly, itchy skin and night blindness, and they also lose their sense of smell and develop heart rhythm abnormalities. Was it possible to develop 'acquired' Refsum's disease as a result of a thiamine deficiency?

Refsum's disease:

↑ Phytanic acid ✕ alpha-oxidation
(no thiamine)

Phytanic acid is a branched chain fatty acid (a fatty acid with a side chain). The thiamine-dependent enzyme, called a lyase, is necessary to remove the side chain. This pathway is termed 'alpha-oxidation'.[21] The more typical breakdown of the non-branched (straight-chain) fatty acids is beta-oxidation, which does not require thiamine. Phytanic acid is found in dairy products and animal fats. I had replaced the sugar in my diet with full fat yoghurt. Feasibly, this could have upset the balance – excess dairy and reduced thiamine – producing toxic byproducts. It seemed to make sense, but there was no proof that thiamine deficiency led to impaired alpha-oxidation. This was still only my hypothesis.

Protein metabolism is also significantly affected by thiamine deficiency. Thiamine is required for the metabolism of the branched-chain amino acids (amino acids with side chains). One such amino acid is leucine. In thiamine deficiency, leucine levels will increase. Leucine has been found to be elevated in obese patients *and* in patients with insulin resistance – or type 2 diabetes – the metabolic syndrome.[22, 23] This was too much to be a coincidence.

Obesity/metabolic syndrome:

↑ Leucine ✕ branched-chain amino acid metabolism

(no thiamine)

The enzyme transketolase is also dependent on thiamine. It features in another important pathway – the pentose phosphate shunt. This pathway is important for both nucleotide production and energy release. Nucleotides link together to form deoxyribonucleic acid and ribonucleic acid – more commonly known as DNA and RNA – the basis of every cell's genes, which are required for growth, reproduction, protein synthesis and repair. Nucleotides are synthesised via another substance called ribose-5-phosphate. In the absence of thiamine, the reduced transketolase activity results in the production of uric acid from ribose-5-phosphate. Uric acid crystallises in the joint, leading to gout. Gout is associated with high alcohol use – alcohol intake reduces thiamine absorption. Increased levels of uric acid are associated with poorer outcome in heart failure.[24] Is this yet another marker of thiamine deficiency (presenting differently in different people)?

Gout:

Ribose-5-phosphate ⟶ ↑ uric acid

reduced transketolase
activity due to
thiamine deficiency

Many high-energy molecules are formed as part of these metabolic pathways. These molecules are charged by functional pathways and discharged when energy is required. The citric acid cycle and the pentose phosphate shunt are important in this respect. The high-energy molecules help to protect the cell from so-called 'oxidative stress'. The damage in diabetes and the metabolic syndrome is thought to occur as a result of 'oxidative stress'; the protective mechanism is broken.

Fructose-6-phosphate, yet another substance in the pentose phosphate pathway, activates pathways known to cause damage in diabetes – the diabetic complications. If there is no thiamine, fructose-6-phosphate increases, and in diabetic patients, a number of downstream linked pathways seem to be activated by this increase in fructose, such as the hexosamine pathway.[25] Diabetic complications, such as nerve damage, eye disease and kidney failure, were once thought to be due to the abnormal binding of glucose to proteins in the body, such as collagen, making it stiffer. This seems to have been an oversimplification, as glucose is the least reactive sugar. It now seems that a build-up of fructose is more likely to cause the damage, and result in the advanced glycation end products seen in diabetics who develop the devastating complications.[26] Fructose is known to be elevated in diabetic patients, and it is also elevated in thiamine deficiency. Is thiamine deficiency, therefore, the primary cause of diabetic complications?

As thiamine deficiency leads to problems with protein synthesis, this would partly explain the muscle wasting I had experienced. As DNA synthesis is compromised, it would make it very difficult for the body to heal itself and fight infections.

Since all the pathways are interlinked, each one impacts others. In the metabolic syndrome, there is a problem with fat deposition. Fructose increases fat production (lipogenesis) in the liver – hence non-alcoholic fatty liver. Fructose is often ingested as high fructose corn syrup, which can be found in many fizzy drinks and sweet snacks. It seems likely that thiamine deficiency could compound this further, increasing fructose or decreasing the metabolism of it. Fat deposition or an increase in 'oxidative stress' triggers an inflammatory response.

The scariest fact is that a lack of thiamine also means that the brain cannot produce neurotransmitters, a key problem in dementia. The neurotransmitter acetylcholine is synthesised from a substance called choline combined with acetyl-CoA – the molecule produced by the action of pyruvate dehydrogenase on pyruvate. In thiamine deficiency, the shortage of acetyl-

CoA leads to a reduction in acetylcholine. The newer dementia drugs try to correct the low levels of acetylcholine by reducing the breakdown of this chemical. Most of the effective ones are based on a class of drugs called cholinesterase inhibitors (anticholinesterases).

$$\text{choline} + \text{acetyl CoA} \longrightarrow \text{acetylcholine}$$

(from pyruvate   (neurotransmitter)
thiamine dependent)

Thiamine deficiency:

↓ acetylcholine

Alzheimer's treatment:
(anticholinesterases)

↑ acetylcholine

Wouldn't it be so much better and simpler to correct the underlying defect, thiamine deficiency, rather than tinker with downstream pathways? Modern medicine was good at putting a sticking plaster on ailments. I was rather pleased that I had tied these details together.

Acetylcholine was also the neurotransmitter used by the parasympathetic autonomic nervous system – the housekeeping system. It opposes the action of the sympathetic system, or the fight and flight response.

Did I have an unopposed fight and flight response? Was this why I felt as though I was in a constant state of panic?

If there was an excess of adrenaline and my acetylcholine had been in short supply, that would certainly explain the agitation and my constant need to keep moving. I remembered the sense of total body relief as the intravenous thiamine had been infused.

Another vague memory was bugging me. Acetylcholine worked by binding to two types of receptors on nerves – muscarinic receptors and nicotinic receptors – causing stimulation. However, the drug nicotine in cigarettes also stimulated nicotinic receptors. My friend Sally was a GP in Cambridge. She was married to the surgeon who saw me about the malrotation. She and I had previously discussed the variations in different types of dementia and Sally had remarked that she saw fewer cases of Parkinson's disease in smokers. It is tricky because smokers were prone to vascular dementia. Smoking actually increases the risk of dementia of all causes. Nicotine activates the acetylcholine receptors directly, increasing transmission at the nicotinic receptors. My mind was reeling with this latest information. Perhaps tenacious smokers were thiamine deficient. It would explain why it was so difficult to quit the drug. And also why many smokers crave sugar after quitting, when the underlying thiamine deficiency, masked by nicotine, takes effect.

In this way, smoking was no different from using cholinesterase inhibitors. It was only effective in one aspect of the thiamine-dependent pathways – the neurotransmission, but had no impact on the overall cellular metabolism. Smoking and cholinesterase inhibitors may improve certain symptoms and delay deterioration in Alzheimer's dementia, but inevitably the disease process would eventually progress, as the underlying cause would not have been rectified.

It was possible to see how the inflammation and the failure to repair DNA and proteins could result in the damage to nerves, brain, liver, heart, blood vessels and joints seen in many degenerative disease processes associated with the metabolic syndrome, dementia, heart disease and even cancer and ageing. The presentation would be particularly variable, as I knew that thiamine deficiency affected individuals in very different ways. This was incredible. But how could I prove it?

★

Now that my vitamin deficiencies had been treated, the surgeon recommended I have an operation to untwist my malrotation and prevent it ever twisting again. Apparently, organising the procedure hadn't been straightforward. Even in a centre of excellence like Addenbrooke's, there was very little operating experience on cases such as mine. A general surgeon was scheduled to do the op, and I don't believe he had done it before. A paediatric consultant surgeon was to assist him. She had done these procedures, albeit not on an adult. My friend, the transplant surgeon, was also helping. He had plenty of experience operating on the small intestines, and every other organ in the abdomen, but just not for this kind of case. I was nervous. Doctors make the worst patients. I was particularly concerned about the anaesthetic. I hated anything that caused brain suppression. Apparently, there was no option. Yet more neurotoxins!

Breath Tests

THE IMMEDIATE POSTOPERATIVE RECOVERY was predictably awful. The pain was excruciating, as the thoracic epidural, which should have given me pain relief and numbness below my mid-chest, fell out when I had rigors in recovery. One of the surgeons informed me immediately after the operation, when I was barely awake, that there were adhesions, but that he couldn't see why my gut wasn't working; perhaps it was 'functional'. There wasn't space in the high-dependency unit so I was cared for in the recovery area outside the main theatres. I clamped my teeth on a metal spoon all night to bear the pain. It seemed to work – somehow. Having had no sleep all night, a series of trainees recognised me as they passed the trolley on their way to start their morning shift. I had been in charge of their training in the past and they wanted to update me on their progress. I didn't want to be rude, or to seem hysterical, so I simply pulled the sheet over my head and refused breakfast, a wash, or any visitors. I was in pain, feeling sick and miserable, and I had effectively been told that the operation had been a failure. I was so disappointed. I wondered why I had bothered. Soups and smoothies for the rest of my life would have been preferable to this.

The following day, however, it was clear that the surgery had been a success and that I could eat a reasonably normal diet without the right upper quadrant discomfort. I could lie flat after eating and not regurgitate or choke. I had a niggle of pain under my left rib cage; apparently, the bowel had been fixed under here to prevent it rotating in the wrong direction again. On returning home 48 hours later, I was able to eat a normal diet and I gradually began to gain weight.

A full-thickness biopsy of my small bowel had been taken during the operation, which, I wasn't surprised to learn, had been reported as normal; the mucosa (lining), the muscles and the serosa (outer layer) were all as they should be. I wondered whether they had managed to look at the small nerve fibres in the gut. The surgeon had been convinced my symptoms were 'functional', whatever that meant!

Unfortunately, the neuropathic pain in my hands and feet did not improve and I continued to visit the unit three times a week for vitamin infusions. There seemed no plan to stop them, which was a good thing as without them I was a wreck.

A diagnosis of bacterial overgrowth was confirmed on a glucose hydrogen breath test, where, after a glucose drink, if there are bacteria present in the small intestines they start proliferating and producing hydrogen, which can be measured in the breath. According to the nurse performing the test, the machine measuring the hydrogen had to recalibrate several times during the procedure. I was producing so much hydrogen in my breath that each time the machine had to step up. The result was not a great surprise; after all, I'd had the lowest vitamin D level I'd ever seen, which I felt sure was a marker of massive bacterial overgrowth. The rise was greater than the usual increase seen in patients with a basically normal gut and a few extra thousand bacteria. My gut had been structurally abnormal for years. My interpretation was that there was definitely bacterial overgrowth.

The high baseline was apparently controversial. I resorted to online literature. There were a number of papers and textbooks reporting that a high fasting breath hydrogen level was indicative of a positive result. I immediately started taking antibiotics, fairly certain that my findings would be confirmed. Antibiotics were associated with a marked improvement in my condition.

A few weeks later, I received a letter from the gastroenterology consultant:

> **'Unfortunately, your breath test gave a bizarre result, the like of which I have never seen. I wonder if the machine was functioning properly. I will make enquiries.'**

The 'breath test' expert in the hospital, who had no direct knowledge of the details of my case, was consulted about the result. He also hadn't seen a result like this one before. Either they had not checked the literature or the erratic spikes, produced when the machine had recalibrated, confused them. They had interpreted the result out of context, without referring to the nurse who conducted the test or the patient. The expert wrote to the gastroenterology consultant I was seeing to explain:

> **'I entirely agree that the result of the hydrogen breath test is quite bizarre, and I think this represents a technical failure. I cannot even see how a procedural failure would give such fluctuating levels, with a peak of over 6000 ppm, when normally a rise of 10 to 20 is regarded as diagnostic.'**

A 'technical failure' meant that they assumed the machine had broken. It hadn't, in fact it had recalibrated several times during the test. They sent the machine away to be repaired and wrote to inform me that the test would need to be repeated once it was in good working order. The test should be repeated off antibiotics. There would be yet more delay and uncertainty. In addition, I knew that the test would now be pointless, as I had already started on antibiotics.

I didn't want any more delay and nor did I want any more tests. As far as I was concerned, it made more sense to treat the patient rather than rely on an ambiguous test result produced on an unreliable machine. Thankfully, I continued to feel better on the antibiotics.

Having read several articles and reviews, which reported that relapse was common, chronic infection highly likely and eradication difficult, I didn't need any more convincing that not only was the bacterial overgrowth secondary to longstanding stagnation in my guts, exacerbated by sugar, but that treatment would require long-term antibiotics. My condition was unlikely to be resolved by simply taking a single course of antibiotics.

More Marvellous Facts
About Thiamine

I HAD A FOLLOW-UP CLINIC APPOINTMENT with the gastroenterology consultant who had requested the breath test. I was really hoping that he would listen to me, see that I was better on the antibiotics and agree that the test had actually shown a positive result. I was hoping that he would recommend long-term cyclical antibiotics: a well-recognised treatment for bacterial overgrowth, particularly one that causes significant malnutrition.

As usual, I had been reading up on thiamine the night before the appointment and as a consequence my mind was bursting with facts about this incredible vitamin: the history, underlying action, uptake, distribution and excretion.

I was disappointed when the consultant told me that my symptoms were not easily explained and that I should continue on the infusions for two further months.

'Eight more weeks!' I moaned quietly to Matthew, who had accompanied me to the appointment. The consultant still wasn't prepared to make any decision on further treatment, such as antibiotics.

I was told that I could have the infusions in the rheumatology day centre, attending three times a week. I had visions of lying on a blue plastic trolley and waiting with all the other patients for the nurse to cannulate me. The consultant didn't approve of the ad hoc administration of the treatment, which was currently taking place in Fraser's office or the anaesthetic room in theatre. It was essentially experimental treatment, without a trial or pathway. I felt sure that once it all became official, there would be obstructions, difficulties and delays. This was my lifeline, and until I worked out what was wrong with me, I couldn't face it being under threat.

I tried to get the consultant to see reason, to listen to me. I mentioned how I was sure I had bacterial overgrowth and thiamine deficiency. I noted the consultant's false smile, or perhaps grimace, and the hollow expression in his eyes. He was clearly utterly disinterested in my theories. My time in the clinic room was coming to a close. He had delivered what he wanted me to hear. He was no longer listening to me. In an exasperated attempt to regain his attention, I told him my idea about thiamine destruction by bacteria.

The evening before, Tom and I had investigated the subject of Roman soldiers for his homework, which he generally needed a lot of assistance with. While he was busy copying words into his exercise book, I came across an explanation for the end of Roman power. Chronic lead poisoning may have resulted in the fall of the Roman Empire. It was suggested that chronic intoxication with lead occurred as a result of drinking wine and grape syrup in lead caskets, as well as breathing in paint. This caused infertility in the ruling classes. In addition to sterility, there were increased numbers of miscarriages, stillbirths and premature labour. I doubted there were delivery suite records, but still the author had a persuasive viewpoint!

Interestingly, thiamine is found in high amounts in semen, which makes sense as sperm rely on a burst of energy to fertilise the egg. My thoughts went off at a tangent; I wondered whether the rise in male infertility in present times and the association of male infertility with alcohol consumption and obesity was due to thiamine deficiency in certain individuals.

It was beginning to fascinate me. Thiamine deficiency could do for populations in developed countries what lead poisoning had done for the Romans. It could mark the end of the human race! My mind was leaping at theories, just as my wits had been clutching at straws.

The consultant continued to look exasperated and bored. I recognised this facial expression all too well; it resembled Matthew's in the early days, when I recounted each new symptom over breakfast.

In desperation, I blurted out, 'Thiamine is found in every tissue, you know – it's even found in semen!'

Both the consultant and the nurse smirked and Matthew hustled me out of the room before I could embarrass myself any further.

Meanwhile, I had been offered little in the way of treatment – in short, I was being fobbed off. I felt humiliated by my outburst and belittled again by a colleague I had previously respected and regarded as knowledgeable, someone who had the reputation of being able to treat any nutritional problem. Quite clearly he thought I was mad and that all my symptoms were 'functional' too. I had done nothing to dismiss this notion.

'Thiamine is found in semen!' I repeated to myself sarcastically. 'Why did you think he would be interested in that little gem of knowledge?' I was berating myself and also felt furious with the consultant.

At home, I scribbled frantically in my diary:

I can't quite believe the outcome of today's consultation
— another two months — that makes it over a year
of suffering with joint pains and no official diagnosis .
. . almost pointless. At this rate my hands will probably

become numb soon and hopefully my brain will too. I vow not to mention joint pains to anyone now and hopefully this technique will work.

By writing my thoughts down and venting my frustrations on paper, I resolved to suffer alone. I stopped taking antibiotics and then had several days off the intravenous thiamine, making a note of my symptoms:

Have definitely become disinterested in things — can't really be bothered. Perhaps list will help, but not sure. Don't feel able to commit to anything, as condition may deteriorate — certainly no faith that I will feel better in next few weeks or months. Ate supper although didn't feel hungry. Have pain in calves bilaterally on standing or sitting.

I was an avid list maker and completer of tasks. The list was supposed to motivate me. I've even been known to add breakfast, bath and hair wash to my things to do, although usually it would be a household chore, such as sort the laundry. Failing to adhere to the list was a definite sign of deterioration. It was an effort to do anything and difficult to maintain hope and positivity. There seemed no point trying to make any plans for the future.

Completely exhausted last night and fell asleep before any of the children. Woke up a few hours later freezing cold and in pain, so made two more boiling hot water bottles — one for hands and one for feet — to add to the bottles already in bed. Also had odd abdominal pains and overactive bowels. Slept well with scalding water bottles on each paw.

Awoke with sore throat and too tired to be aware of pain until I moved — pain in ankles, hands and feet all day. By the end of the day (of not walking too far but sitting in office), feet and legs feel as though I have been on a 100km route march and shooting sensations radiating up both legs (where pain was yesterday but also anteriorly). Hands feel weak. It hurts to hold steering wheel. Wrists more painful. Energy levels beginning to sap — tread is becoming heavier, haven't tripped yet but feel as though have to place feet carefully each step.

I was now fully aware of the symptoms of beriberi and was watching for them. It was worrying how quickly all my symptoms returned.

Feel slightly odd, not sure if it is just tiredness. Having to concentrate to do anything, even write. Just feel like sleeping (or crying). No appetite, windy tummy, don't feel like opening bowels. Unusual for me — wonder if I'm becoming constipated again? Took new glasses off as pink edges starting to glare and almost confuse me. As if brain could not decipher change with new rim.

I had deteriorated. I was giving up. I was scared. But scared of what? Dying? I confronted myself with the question. What was actually worrying me?

No, I was actually more scared of living like this and becoming an increasing burden to my family and children. I was worried that I would deteriorate until I no longer recognised my own kids. I was being brutally honest with myself.

★

I remembered a patient I had seen who attended the Emergency Department on numerous occasions with 'falls due to alcohol intoxication.' This patient had then fallen and sustained an intracranial bleed. Unfortunately, even though the neurosurgery had managed to clear the large clot, several weeks later, when she returned from the local neurosurgical centre, she had a complete loss of memory. This was the worst case of Korsakoff's dementia I had ever seen. The doctors treating her for falls had not given her intravenous thiamine, which may have prevented the permanent brain damage. They had probably been focusing on the fact that she had a serious head injury and needed transferring to the local neurosurgical unit for brain surgery. I remembered the patient's young daughter visiting her in the side room on the ward. The patient was unable to recognise this poor child, her own daughter.

My despair returned. I was still having the intravenous vitamins three times a week. It was now prescribed for me to have at home, and was hooked up to the picture rail. Matthew and I thought it less than ideal, but there seemed no alternative. I continued writing my thoughts in the diary:

Am going over and over things in my mind and having rather dark thoughts — I do not want any more Pabrinex or antibiotics until a diagnosis has been made. I will need to be admitted to have Pabrinex. I do not want to be resuscitated if I have brain damage. I do not want active treatment if I have permanent brain damage, e.g. Korsakoff's. I would like my organs to be used to help some other poor soul at the mercy of the medical profession. I would like my stories and this published so that other victims with similar unmeasurable problems with their guts can at least be taken seriously.

I have pains in my shoulder. I have removed my belt as my stomach is tender and bloated and much less active, and my wrists have shooting pains when I try to do up the belt.

I have started shouting at the kids, which makes me upset. If I am to be like this forever, I do feel they would be better off without me. Life is not worth living like this.

Reading up on thiamine deficiency again — stores last as little as 3/52. No thiamine intake for 6/52 has resulted in death in patients on TPN.

As a water-soluble vitamin, thiamine is not stored for long in the body – perhaps three to six weeks. Total parenteral nutrition (TPN) is the nutrition given through the vein, avoiding the gut completely. It is synthesised to have the correct proportions of glucose, amino acids and fatty acids, as well as all the essential vitamins, including thiamine. If thiamine has been inadvertently missed out then death occurs in six weeks.

Day 3 off (infusions) I think — 11 hrs in bed, just feel weak — wrists and ankles worse now. Developing twitches in thigh now, pain in fingers switching on indicators, pains in calf muscles. Beginning to operate on autopilot, unable to maintain train of thought, forget what I am doing all the time — start doing something and forget in the middle. Start saying things and forget in the middle. Am positive, though, as I have decided to

get second opinion and to write living will stating that I
do not want to be resuscitated in the event of cardiac
arrest, and also that I do not wish for active treatment
if I develop Korsakoff's syndrome. This would include
treatments of any infections. Hand and wrist hurts to
write. Just feel very tired all the time. Still do not want
to live like this, if this is going to be my quality of life
— would rather die. For a number of reasons better off
dead. Had been upset at the thought of not seeing the
children grow up, but actually think they would be better
off without me like this.

I clearly had memory problems and was unable to recall that
I had already written down in my diary these concerns. I
was repeating myself and not realising it. I felt much calmer,
though, it was almost a relief to admit that I was not afraid
to die and that I would definitely not wish to be resuscitated.

Once I am gone, leave me be, let me slip away. I would
not wish to continue with impairments and right now
I have significant impairments, restricting my life and
impacting those near to me.

Meanwhile, life continued and the children needed their
mother. Emily was attending the Junior Guildhall School of
Music and Drama in London, playing piano and viola. She
was too young to make her way unaccompanied and so either
Matthew or I would travel down on the train with her and
wait in the Barbican until she had finished. As Matthew was
working, I also had to take the boys with me, and I decided
the best way to entertain them would be a visit to the nearby
Museum of London.

I walked slowly through the museum, watching the boys flit from one area to another, looking at displays on the Great Fire of London and the Plague. I must have taken my eyes off them for a few seconds. I suddenly realised Edward was missing.

'Where's your brother?' I snapped at Tom. I was panicking. Surely he had just wandered off, but things happen . . .

We looked around the stands nearby, but he'd gone.

'You go back that way,' I said to Tom. 'I'll go this way.' I sent him off, unsure whether this was sensible, but figuring he would be quicker than me.

All the time I was thinking to myself, *He's gone! I must find him.*

My legs felt like two lead weights, as though I was dragging them through sinking mud, heavy yet featherweight, powerless and weak. The dark walls were oppressive. The displays, which had been engaging, were now cluttering my vision. I had walked through the level we had been viewing and was back in the entrance hall waiting for Tom and wondering whether I should go down to the next level. I sat down on some steps.

I tried to motivate myself to go down the stairs, trying to muster the energy, telling myself I had to get up. I tried to push myself. *I can't, I can't do it. Where's he gone?* I felt desperate. *I feel so weak.* Tom returned, shaking his head.

'Go and find him!' I shouted.

In a flash, I was irritable and unnecessarily short with Tom.

'He shouldn't have disappeared like that,' I said, more quietly, as I shook my head in despair, feeling guilty.

This was my fault. Would I never learn?

I had done too much. I was too tired to walk any further so I just stayed on the steps.

'Can we help?' a young man asked. He was wearing a uniform and leaning over me.

'Yes, thank you! It's my son. He's missing,' I explained.

When Edward was eventually found the relief was incredible. The staff had been so kind, although it was Tom who was uncharacteristically responsible for finding his brother – locating him trying on helmets in the Roman section in the basement.

I had documented the symptoms, minus the drama, in my diary:

Day 4. Awoke feeling just tired, effort to get going. London trip today and managed to walk to Barbican/ Guildhall and round Museum of London, but legs felt like lead. Had to sit down several times. Calves painful rather than feet, although aware of pain in feet when I stop. It just feels as though I have run a marathon. Palms of hands actually feel tender.

My situation was hopeless. I wasn't panicking, though; I was too exhausted to waste the emotional energy. I stuck to my word and wrote my own version of a living will, which I folded neatly and stored in the back of my diary.

Day 5. Flickering in buttocks, pain in calves and lateral aspects of thighs. Also pain radiating up inner aspect (ulnar) of elbows. Sharp pains in wrists and proximal MCP (metacarpophalangeal joints at the base of the fingers) all the time — feel tender on pressure but also when using hand to hold things, e.g., book, pen, especially thumb. Now

beginning to feel restless — tremor — coffee probably
not helped but want to be active not sit, even if nothing
to do — finding it difficult to just sit. Feeling cross at
nothing, e.g., other drivers, work — previously not cared
or easy going, now feel on edge.

I had returned to work on a minimally part-time basis, with no on-call. The Occupational Health Department had been helpful, and it was recognised that I had a disability. My colleagues were also supportive. I was effectively being supervised more than the medical students, and I was unable to do any of the practical procedures, such as taking blood, as I was too shaky and couldn't feel my hands.

Day 6. Monday. Really beginning to feel quite unwell and
had to drag myself out of bed. Sore throat turned into
irritating, productive cough with intermittent right-sided
chest pain — not too low yet. Feeling very lethargic.
Ankles and hands worse today, still flickering muscles in
legs. Noticeable ankle pain when driving car and hands
tender when holding the steering wheel — not actually
tender but painful to grip things — and to stretch hand
open. Now craving sugar just to keep going. Weight
started to fall — constipated — i.e., no natural bowel
movement without assistance. Feel as though walking in
a cloud — not quite here. Still able to describe symptoms
— these are consuming most of my thoughts. Not quite
with it. It's an effort to concentrate. Last night, for the
first time, felt restless and had 'shakes' or 'palpitations'.
Heart rate not faster but attacks limited by carotid
sinus massage — whole body feels as though it is shaking
— comes on suddenly, at night. Cross with children's

squabbles last night — short tempered and irritable. Continued pain in ankles when walking, and backs of hands. Just wondered if this, and fasciculations, are actually vit D deficiency again, as opposed to just thiamine. Will start 5000U vit D tomorrow am. Last two occasions im [intramuscular] vit D has worn off after 1-2/52, now it is 10+ days since last im jab.

Day 10. Constant pain in hands and calves, particularly at night; pins and needles last night, feel awful — now suffering, on autopilot — no energy, feel weak, falling over, bumping into things, tripping up on flat surfaces — need to remember to pick feet up but no obvious foot drop. Pain in upper arms and thighs — cold all the time, wearing many layers, two hot water bottles at night to help pain and keep warm.

My cough had worsened. I was producing green phlegm and had a fever and chest pain. It was clear that I needed antibiotics.

'Started antibiotics (1 week course)

Day 1: I know I feel different.

Day 2: My head feels clearer.

Day 3: Busy day at a hockey tournament. Normally I would start flagging and have to sit down, but even at the end I could walk back to the car without staggering or struggling. I am still aware of a slight burning sensation in my hands, but it didn't wake me, I just knew it was there when I got up and I can feel it when I sit still and think about it. It is much less now. I feel able to do things, to make plans and even feel like going for a run — I won't because I think it would be foolhardy until the sensation in my hands and feet has returned to normal. I do feel much more like myself, more positive, some energy back. Bowels had been incredibly underactive but now I'm passing solid motions, not feeling need to strain. Thirsty but high dose vitamin D seems to affect this. If I reduce to 10000U I get joint pains and less thirst. 15000U means joints and fasciculations are better but I feel really thirsty. Drinking 1-1.5 L overnight each night. Wore new boots for the first time yesterday and able to cope with leather rather than fur lined boots I've worn recently.

Day 5: I've been on antibiotics for five days now and I feel great, happy to be alive and enthusiastic. I wanted to go to work this morning. I have energy. I can chivvy the children and cope with everyday stresses without getting terribly shaky. I walked up two flights of stairs without feeling like collapsing at the top. My skin has cleared up. I have normal, solid bowel motions. I don't have constant gurgling in my gut. I actually have an appetite. I was aroused during intercourse for the first time in months, possibly years. I feel human. I do have a prickly sensation in my hands. I don't feel cold all the time. My hair feels soft. I have had no problems swallowing.

10th day off antibiotics: Gurgling in gut constant, no MMC (migrating motor complex — the electrical activity in the gut that stimulates peristalsis and normal gut action) — BO (bowels open) squidgy, every time I pass urine I feel as though not emptying, bloated I guess, dyspepsia, thirsty, particularly at night, hands ache, feet too, also twitching again, started antibiotics, can't wait . . .

There was a definite and repeatable pattern. Antibiotics and thiamine with vitamin D supplementation resolved my symptoms, which returned once the antibiotics stopped. Off them I could feel my guts stop working. The peristaltic action moves the contents of the gut along and usually results in the desire to defecate. This wasn't happening. I just had this constant gurgling and sense of disquiet. Soon after restarting antibiotics, the situation returned to normal.

As the gastroenterologist hadn't wanted to treat me, I reckoned I had two choices: I could either do nothing and continue to suffer, or I could seek a second opinion.

In my head, I could hear my nana telling me, 'There is no such word as can't!'

I persuaded myself that I *must* do it.

Nothing was insurmountable. I had to find a way.

I vowed: *I will fight this.*

I sought further advice, this time from a friend and gastroenterology colleague in Oxford. I hadn't previously felt able to contact her, as until now I had been unable to speak coherently on the telephone. I explained my symptoms, the results of the tests and the improvement when taking antibiotics.

'My dear, you have bacterial overgrowth,' Deborah said. 'It's fairly obvious. You need cyclical antibiotics.'

The plan was to cycle the antibiotics every fortnight, alternating between co-amoxiclav, metronidazole, doxycycline and clarithromycin. I started the treatment. It worked. Now I could be a mother, wife, doctor – not an invalid, patient, mental case.

Mad Bowel Disease

I HADN'T ALWAYS WANTED TO BE A DOCTOR, just as I hadn't always wanted to be a gastroenterologist. I was interested in science and enjoyed solving problems. I found using a sequence of experiments in A-Level chemistry to identify a secret chemical compound thrilling, but this wasn't the vibe I managed to get across at the interview for medical school. The girl being interviewed before me had written on her application form that she enjoyed cooking. She was therefore asked how to make spaghetti Bolognese. She laughed as she recounted this to me; she hadn't a clue how to make the dish, and I surmised from her story that my interview would be a relaxed affair. As I walked into the interview room I came face to face with two men in dark grey suits.

'Are you interested in politics?' one of them asked as I sat down.

I replied that no, I wasn't particularly interested, and I was rather perplexed by the question – I hadn't mentioned politics on my application form. I didn't really understand why they were asking this. Naively, I didn't think politics should interfere with good healthcare.

'Who is Colonel Gaddafi?' was the next question.

I was thrown. I let my temper get the better of me. How on earth was this relevant to medicine?

'An African leader,' I replied.

I was being vague on purpose, trying not to sound cross or flustered. I couldn't be certain that he was Libyan. I was worried about getting it wrong and being questioned even further about world politics. I was now glowing with an ember of embarrassment, anger simmering just below the surface, feeling the redness extend across my face. I was not good at hiding my feelings. All those years in amateur dramatics and acting in school plays couldn't help me in this situation.

The second interviewer then took to the stage. 'What would you do if someone threw a hand grenade at you in an airport?' he smirked, clearly enjoying intimidating me.

I didn't know what to say. I was confused and even a little irritated as to why this would be useful knowledge for a doctor. After recounting the interview questions to friends, I was offered many quips.

'Pull the pin and throw it back!'

'Duck!'

But during the interview I'd said nothing. How was I supposed to respond? Were they testing my sense of humour? I'm sure this kind of questioning would be strongly discouraged nowadays, on many grounds. Perhaps this was how they taught medicine, too, by ritual humiliation.

As a child, I'd initially thought how great it would be to become a vet; not only because of treating cute, furry pets, but also because I loved all animals and enjoyed being outdoors. My father had studied to be a farm manager, but with one sweeping statement dismissed my career proposal as ridiculous. 'You'll have to put your hand inside a cow's bottom,' he'd said.

Aged just eight at the time, I can't remember the exact phrase, but this was definitely the sentiment. I was shocked and understandably put off veterinary science for life. Little did I know then that in the years to come I would be inserting long black flexible telescopes around the large bowel of humans, as I performed colonoscopies. Incidentally, it was much more difficult to complete these examinations on women. Somehow they seemed to have much longer, more tortuous bowels. I suppose this must be a design flaw, or maybe it was intentional so that the colon can move out of the way of an enlarging uterus during pregnancy. Either way, it made for a trying time as a colonoscopist. I would dread turning up to work to find that the five patients on my colonoscopy list were all female, after requesting a lady doctor, and that they didn't want sedation. Consequently, these sessions took hours.

Worse still was the instrument. I found it much easier to use the paediatric colonoscope, which had smaller controls and fitted my hands better. At the time there was only one of these in the unit, and my colleagues often used it for difficult cases involving strictures. The other colonoscopes were easier to use if you had large hands. My colleagues, being mostly male, had not seen the point of purchasing any more of the paediatric colonoscopes. The perks of being one of only two female endoscopists in the unit!

Subconsciously, I suppose my interest in guts must have been because of the abdominal symptoms I'd had all my life. The upside of this abdominal complaint was that I had never been overweight. In fact, I generally struggled to gain pounds. It had never been easy to overeat. After any illness or period of weight loss, I could only gain weight slowly, having to opt for higher calorie foods and eating more regularly. The other reason I was attracted to my speciality was probably the constant gurgling of my guts. I had grown up with the noisiest of intestines. It was as if they had a mind of their own.

I was also used to passing very frequent, often urgent motions, mostly liquid. It was just something I was used to. It's just not something that is discussed, even amongst close friends or with a partner.

For years I had blamed eating excess fruit, an alteration in my diet, or even the water supply – whatever seemed most likely whenever my bowels were particularly bad. Matthew tended to avoid mentioning my bowels, although when my guts were at their most active he sometimes had to turn up the sound on the television to avoid missing the dialogue on a film. There were three in our marriage – Matthew, me and my guts, which announced their presence at the most inopportune moments. Matthew rarely had problems with his bowels. When the children were babies and suffered with horrendous diarrhoea caused by the usual viral gastroenteritis infections, it was me who would succumb.

'How are you feeling? I hope you don't get it,' I would say, completely drained and dehydrated, but still trying to soldier on.

'I think I have it already,' he'd reply in a jovial manner.

'Oh no!' I would say, really concerned, not only for his welfare, but because now we would all be incapacitated. And the washing! It would be impossible to keep up with this. I had already been struggling to dry the baby's clothes.

'I've just done a smelly fart!' he'd say, half serious.

As my illness progressed, my symptoms changed and I became constipated. I felt bloated and struggled to open my bowels, although my stools were still not properly formed. Thinking back, I realised that this happened some time after I stopped taking regular courses of antibiotics for the chest infections. It is well recognised that malabsorption is associated with diarrhoea, but little known that advanced malabsorption actually causes constipation.

Being a consultant with an interest in gastroenterology, I had spent my life reassuring patients, after investigations had produced no abnormal results, that there really was nothing wrong with their bowels. I would advise them to drink more water, take more fibre, eat less fibre, eat more vegetables, eat fewer vegetables, or drink even more water. Other treatments for 'irritable bowels' included low-dose anti-depression medication, which might help with the discomfort, but I'm sure exacerbated the underlying condition. I could now see that my well-meaning advice was no better than homeopathic medicine, and that the treatments on offer through the NHS were potentially detrimental.

Endless research into the condition irritable bowel syndrome had shown that the affected guts were normal – the muscle layer was normal, the mucosal lining was normal, the blood vessels were normal, the intestines were normal, as were the nerves. Unlike most of my patients, I even had a biopsy during surgery to demonstrate that my intestines were normal throughout, so any bowel symptoms I had were simply functional.

So what does 'functional' mean? Well, the way most gastroenterologists say it, you would think it was caused by an abnormal brain function: a figment of the patient's functional or dysfunctional imagination. I was adamant that I didn't want to discuss my problems with any gastroenterologist and risk being labelled with an even larger sign – one that proclaimed 'Mad Bowel Disease.'

Strangely, my bowels improved on the cyclical antibiotics. In fact, they were quieter than they had ever been, and as regular as clockwork, which made me think that there could be a connection. Was there a link between irritable bowel syndrome and bacterial overgrowth?

There were other clues, too. I met with a friend and work colleague, Sarah-Jane, after not seeing her for many months. She was a paediatrician, so our paths didn't often cross. I was sorry to hear that her mother had been unwell and that she had been having a really difficult time. Her mother had been admitted to a nursing home, as she had developed rapid onset dementia and had become aggressive towards her husband, Sarah-Jane's stepfather. Sadly, she didn't even recognise her daughter. Whilst driving back home from Leeds, Sarah-Jane had crashed the car. She was trying to be in too many places at once and enacting too many roles: mother, wife, doctor and dutiful daughter. It was her throwaway comment and nonverbal gesture as we parted company that struck a chord.

'She's always had functional problems, you know, IBS, fibromyalgia. She's always had problems,' Sarah-Jane explained, her eyebrows lifting a touch. She gave her head a slight shake and shrugged her shoulders – all subtle signs that the relationship had been difficult, mainly because of her mother's 'health' problems. I made a note to myself, as I was still intrigued by the link between gut symptoms and my hypothesis about the cause of dementia.

I found the search easy once I employed the correct term and abbreviation – small intestinal bacterial overgrowth, or SIBO for short. There was an association between bacterial overgrowth and irritable bowel syndrome, but it seemed that there were believers (converts like myself) and non-believers ('flat earthers' who simply did not accept a different explanation).

Much of the work had been done in patients with diabetes and diarrhoea, for once actually described as diabetic-associated diarrhoea, rather than some Latin term no one could remember and certainly couldn't spell. However, my reading had uncovered something really interesting and important. I had to share this with Matthew.

We were sitting in the new kitchen, in the L-shaped barn overlooking the courtyard. It was breakfast time.

'Bob said he'd plant some more apple trees to replace the ones we lost,' Matthew said, whilst pouring us both a mug of tea. 'I think a couple of Spartans would be nice.' He took a large bite of his toast with orange marmalade and slurped the hot tea.

'That'll be nice,' I responded. We'd had Spartans in Nana's garden. They produced small, shiny red apples, with crisp, cream flesh. I wanted to update him on my news.

'I read up on IBS last night and diabetic diarrhoea . . . '

There was a snort followed by a slight choke and cough. Matthew's eyes were watering. Unfortunately, he did not welcome my revelation. It seemed I had crossed the line regarding suitable topics for discussion at mealtimes, even though it wasn't my own bowels I was describing. Perhaps that was the problem, the mental image of an overweight diabetic with foot ulcers and dodgy bowels was more than Matthew could cope with whilst eating his toast. Metaphorically, I would have to go underground. This subject had not passed the breakfast table test. I made a mental note that it would not be appropriate dinner party conversation either. I was finding it very difficult to restrain myself when these thoughts were occupying so much of my waking hours.

Even the children were beginning to tire of my constant mention of thiamine. Initially, they were so relieved to have Mum back that I was allowed a certain freedom of thought and speech. I was sure they must have noticed that I had changed and was no longer 'shouty mummy'. It became a bit of a joke that whenever I asked a simple homework question, such as 'What do plant cells make in chloroplasts?' the standard response was, 'Is the answer thiamine?' This was even if I had asked about something entirely different, which occasionally I did manage to do.

My fascinating discovery was that bacterial overgrowth is associated with autonomic neuropathy (nerve damage to the small nerve fibres in the body).[27] The autonomic nerves control the autonomic functions in the body, the ones animals have no control over: bodily functions, such as sweating, heart rate and, of course, our guts; the housekeeping functions – controlled by the parasympathetic nerves; and the fight and flight response – controlled by the sympathetic nerves. The tests showed that by recording how the gut moves it is possible to detect changes in the gut motion in diabetic patients who are troubled with diarrhoea, and that these changes are rectified with antibiotics.[28] It isn't just the movement through the gut that improves with antibiotics, the diarrhoea also improves.[29]

I spoke to Nick, a colleague at the hospital who specialised in endocrinology and could cope with discussing diarrhoea. He was well aware of this association, but somehow the gastroenterologists weren't so convinced. Not only was the bacterial overgrowth causing diarrhoea – perhaps I should rephrase that, in my excitement, I was assuming a causal relationship – not only was the bacterial overgrowth associated with diarrhoea, but the daily insulin requirement was higher in patients with autonomic neuropathy, as well as those with bacterial overgrowth.[27] Diabetic patients with small intestinal bacterial overgrowth that had been treated with antibiotics subsequently required less insulin. In simple terms, this meant that diabetes improved on antibiotics.

Bingo! A result! I was definitely getting somewhere. But I was not diabetic, so there was a slight blip in my argument. Back to the literature!

Further reading showed an association between bacterial overgrowth and intestinal dysmotility in obese, mostly non-diabetic patients.[30, 31] Interestingly, these patients were more likely to have insulin resistance (or pre-type 2 diabetes, differentiating it from the 'first' type of diabetes that is due to a lack of insulin – in type 2 diabetes there is plenty of insulin, but the cells don't respond appropriately to it).[32] Bacterial overgrowth, intestinal dysmotility and insulin resistance are all associated. Insulin resistance is the hallmark of the metabolic syndrome.

So far so good! I was encouraged by my latest find. But I wasn't overweight, either. I was going to have to try harder if I was going to succeed in convincing anyone of my ideas, when even my 'n=1' – my observational study of one person – didn't match any identifiable patterns of disease.

I really needed to find some evidence of an association between irritable bowel and bacterial overgrowth in patients without diabetes or obesity. My hunch was right.[33, 34] Much of the work had been done in Italy, where an antibiotic named rifaximin had been developed. This antibiotic was now being used in several countries to treat patients suffering from irritable bowels, as well as other indications, such as gastrointestinal infections. Drug company-funded research always aroused a certain amount of suspicion, but there seemed to be reasonable evidence to support the use of the drug.

Diarrhoea-predominant irritable bowel syndrome was strongly associated with bacterial overgrowth and also with dysmotility and fasciculations (the muscle twitches or restless legs).[35] Patients' irritable bowel symptoms responded to treatment with rifaximin[33], and their fasciculations also responded to the antibiotic therapy.[36] It seemed that the main benefit of this antibiotic was that the resistant rates were low. In addition, as it wasn't absorbed, its effect was restricted to the gut rather than entering the circulation.

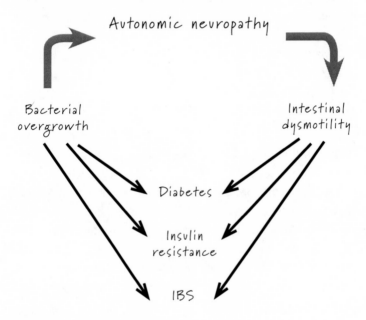

Through my research, I felt sure I had discovered something important. If there was a connection between diabetes, bacterial overgrowth and *thiamine deficiency*, then this was a big – actually a monumental – discovery. I was excited.

There was seldom a day when there wasn't a relevant article in the media.

Diabetes could bankrupt the NHS

Diabetes cases soar 60% in a decade

It didn't take me long to find data to support the other half of the equation, or rather circle, linking thiamine deficiency to diabetes. Thiamine deficiency had been linked to vascular complications in diabetic patients.[37] Not only did antibiotic treatment improve diabetic control, but high-dose thiamine treatment also prevented diabetes-associated kidney damage[38], alleviated hyperglycaemia and improved diabetic control.[39] The two mechanisms of disease – small intestinal bacterial overgrowth and thiamine deficiency – seemed to be closely linked through autonomic neuropathy and gut dysmotility. It wasn't the kind of proof many scientists would accept, but it was certainly strong circumstantial evidence.

What did come as a bit of a surprise was to find out that in many patients with interlinked syndromes, such as restless leg syndrome, fibromyalgia and irritable bowel syndrome, symptoms such as fatigue, sleep disturbance and cognitive problems were incredibly common. These are all recognisable symptoms of thiamine deficiency. Interestingly, in one trial, I discovered that fibromyalgia patients had responded to high-dose intravenous thiamine treatment.[40] On this occasion n=3.

These fortunate patients had found a doctor like Fraser, who was prepared to try experimental treatment. Needless to say, this study hadn't been performed in England. It would be too difficult to get the funding for such a cheap treatment – nowadays drug companies fund many of the studies. I felt sure that any study we tried to instigate would flop at the ethical approval stage. Red tape would prevent Fraser and I administering intravenous vitamins as part of a study to see if there was an identifiable benefit. At the very least we would need to measure thiamine levels, which would require funding. Doctors working on wards are seldom able to perform research these days. It's a different world from my training in Southampton, when the lab was just round the corner from the ward and novel ideas for research could be formulated, followed up and achieved, with academics undertaking research often being given a reduced clinical schedule.

The fatigue was easy to explain, as thiamine deficiency leads to a failure to release sufficient energy from sugar. If these patients had experienced the same symptoms as me, the temptation to slip a bit of sugar into a cup of tea or snack on a biscuit would have been too great. But this extra calorie and sugar intake would further increase small intestinal bacterial overgrowth, thus perpetuating the problem.

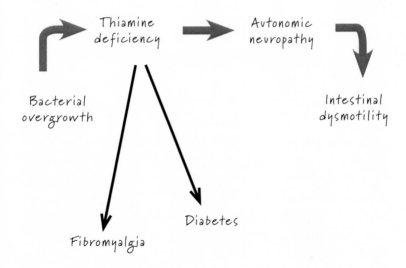

Now that I could complete the circle, I felt vindicated. I'd discovered that thiamine deficiency causes an autonomic neuropathy, delaying gastrointestinal transit. Reduced intestinal motility increases the risk of bacterial overgrowth. Thiamine deficiency leads to fatigue and encourages sugar intake. Sugary supplements increase bacteria in static guts. My hypothesis was that bacteria must breakdown or consume thiamine, exacerbating the thiamine deficiency.

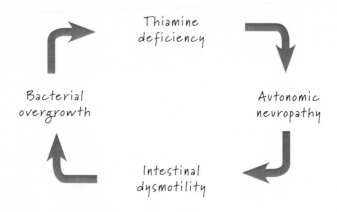

Thiamine deficiency

Bacterial overgrowth

Autonomic neuropathy

Intestinal dysmotility

I researched a definition of small intestinal bacterial overgrowth. It wasn't a commonly used term and there didn't seem to be any consensus on just how many bacteria could be present in the small intestines before it was considered a disease. I wondered again whether it was the type rather than the number that was more important. Mechanical stasis is the most common cause of small intestinal bacterial overgrowth, and I had already discovered that this is usually postsurgical. Other causes listed included diabetes, presumably because of the associated nerve damage and the ensuing stasis.

Scleroderma was also a recognised cause. In this connective tissue disease, the normal, soft, supple mucosa in the gut is replaced with stiff collagen or scar tissue, causing stasis. Then there was a list of miscellaneous causes, such as AIDS, chronic pancreatitis, liver cirrhosis and immunodeficiencies. These associated diseases were generally thought to be due to a reduced ability to fight infections.

My health was continuing to improve and I felt that my memory and concentration were definitely recovering. Finally, I could acknowledge that I was now pain free for most of the time, but occasionally I noticed the neuralgia in my hands returning. It was difficult to be certain of this, but I would rub my hands together, almost unaware that I was doing so. Even Matthew noticed. I was disappointed, but not totally surprised – antibiotic resistance is well documented and I presumed that I was developing resistance. One by one the antibiotics stopped working and I was left taking single therapy doxycycline, which thankfully, for the time being anyway, still seemed to work.

Life as a Chorister

THE CHILDREN WERE NOW ALL ATTENDING the school in the city centre, and Edward was a chorister in the cathedral associated with it. The Cathedral Close was an oasis of calm and quiet in the centre of the town, except for school drop off and during breaktime, when there was a medley of sounds: constant chattering, the patter of footfall and the grating of wheelie sports bags over cobbled pathways. The majestic cathedral occupied a large space between the Bishop's Palace and Gardens, the houses in The Close and the school.

Edward wasn't required to board, but he had to rehearse before and after school each day, and sing evensong three evenings a week in addition to two services every Sunday. With the help of our au pair, it was possible to arrange between us the pickups at different times, following the various after-school activities.

Then our au pair left to return to Riga, Latvia, after living with us for three years. I'm sure medals have been awarded for lesser achievements. She was amazing and really helped when I underwent the surgery. She was incredibly patient with the children and was frequently called upon to deliver to the school forgotten homework, sports kits or musical instruments in time for deadlines, games or music lessons, as well as getting spare keys to Matthew when he locked himself out. She was able to anticipate issues and sort out glitches before they became major problems. It was like having a wife or a personal assistant at home (which, working for the NHS, was more than I had at work).

After the au pair left, there was a general increase in the level of chaos. Emily and Edward were particularly disorganised. Emily would regularly require items to be brought to school. Conversely, Edward would take them to school, but forget to bring them home afterwards. It was a fairly standard procedure to visit the lower school cloakroom once a week to pick up Edward's belongings. He once managed to lose two pairs of trainers in the space of a day. He acquired clothes from his siblings, so fortunately had plenty of spares, but it was common practice to find all four of his coats on the floor in the school cloakroom.

Shoes were a particular problem, because one sure way of making certain you didn't have to stop to take your shoes off when you ran indoors, leaving all the doors open, was to not wear any. I recall taking Edward and his siblings into town. I invented a new rule, which helped everyone get ready promptly, but which particularly helped the au pair. The boys were only allowed to play electronic games on their gadgets in the car. This meant that they would dash outside as soon as a journey was so much as hinted at. This left just the two teenage girls to coerce out of the house, and, as long as it wasn't early morning (any time before 11.30 am), they were usually civilised.

The boys were duly playing Mario Kart in the back of the car, with Emily sitting in the front doing her makeup, when Anna announced that Edward wasn't wearing any shoes. Unfortunately, we were already 30 minutes late for Anna to meet her friends and 15 minutes into our journey. By quick calculation, I worked out there wasn't enough time to turn around and that a pair of cheap shoes would probably cost less than the wasted fuel. We visited the nearest shoe-selling place as soon as we reached town. The staff in the department store weren't used to their customers walking into the store barefoot to purchase a pair of Crocs!

This was the first of many shoe incidents. Edward didn't learn from his mistakes. There had been the 'wellies-in-evensong' parade, which had been frowned upon by the Dean. Once a week, on Friday, there is no organ accompanying the choir, so the voices resonate through the lofty expanse. Apparently, on this particular occasion, the singing was beautiful, but the flapping and clomping sound of wellies echoing throughout the magnificent edifice as the choristers walked in 'silent' formation understandably ruined the moment.

The next time Edward forgot his shoes he was made to wear socks, which were at least quiet, even if they were a little chilly underfoot on the flagstones of the cathedral's main aisle. At the start of the term, he wore his brand new shoes, which had small cars hidden in the soles. Obviously, these were the ones Edward had chosen himself. What little boy wouldn't choose a pair of shoes with small plastic cars hidden inside them, as opposed to the usual boring, toy-less ones?

It was proving a major ordeal to juggle working full-time, four children and a husband without any help. I remember feeling really proud when I finally succeeded in leaving Edward at the song school, the building the choristers used for rehearsals, with a full, correct uniform, complete with coat and shiny new black shoes. I was so disappointed when I picked him up only to learn that he had been in trouble yet again. Undoubtedly, this was the pièce de résistance. His latest transgression had been realised all too late during his participation in the candlelit service. If only they had noticed it before the choristers entered in procession into the cathedral, then he could have gone in socks. Instead, flashing red lights emitted like Belisha beacons from his new shoes – lights which shone across the flagstones for all the congregation and the Dean and Chapter to see. It was even more noticeable because it was a processional service, with the choristers walking up and down the cathedral and singing at the high alter and the west door. At other services, his feet would have been hidden behind the choir stalls. He couldn't have chosen a worse occasion to showcase his new footwear.

After that incident, the lights on his shoes were taped up. Unfortunately, the tape required reapplying regularly, as it tended to become unstuck following dips in puddles. Several months and many services later, it was discovered that by using a button on the side of each shoe it was possible to switch off the flashing lights!

Dementia Friend

EMILY AND ANNA WERE IN THE SAME YEAR at school. It hadn't been planned, but moving schools at an awkward time meant that Anna had to move up a year. As doctors, we had moved jobs and house frequently. Anna was coping well, but Emily hated it. They both had GCSEs looming and the additional stress of competition was taking its toll on our eldest. I hoped that once they started sixth form they would study different subjects and any sibling rivalry would diminish. That plan was kiboshed by a shared knack for languages. Anna thrived in sixth form. She enjoyed reading and in addition to her languages was studying English and classics. Neither of the girls had any desire to pursue science. Clearly the apple experiment at Sir Isaac Newton's farm museum all those years ago hadn't instilled a deep interest in questioning the theory of everything.

The postman delivered very little mail to our town address, as it was only our temporary home. We had rented the small house to use weekdays during term time. The package the postman delivered was addressed to Anna. She opened it and admitted that she had signed up to be a 'dementia friend.' The envelope contained booklets and a badge, along with the inevitable request for funds. She had used her initiative. It had actually been a really grown-up thing to do, but I was initially critical, not of Anna, but of the fact that the glossy booklet must have been expensive to produce and was supposed to give sensible advice. I felt the sort of information it contained could easily have been presented on the internet for a fraction of the cost. I thought the families of people with Alzheimer's needed more. They would benefit from the personal touch – human interaction – rather than a leaflet. I also felt the money would have been better invested seeking the cause and treating the underlying condition. I instantly regretted my initial response, which must have seemed dismissive. Anna was only trying to help. I'm sure she did it for me.

I was only too aware of the risks posed by patients who have Alzheimer's. There was the case of 'meths' poisoning. A couple with the disease had won a bottle of 'white vermouth' in a raffle and promptly shared it at home. Unfortunately, they hadn't questioned why it was blue. It had been donated to the raffle, and at some point someone must have refilled the vermouth bottle with methylated spirit. They were in a terrible state, particularly the wife. The husband was treated with an ethanol infusion on the ward – the poor chap was terribly disinhibited and propositioned all the nursing staff.

Over the years, there had been several cases of smoke inhalation on the unit. My mother too had recounted a recent scare when the lady downstairs in her apartment block put her socks in the microwave. The fire brigade had to be contacted when the kitchen filled with smoke.

Anna's dementia leaflet didn't mention checking the booze cabinet or getting rid of the microwave, but it did suggest that patients with dementia might be more comfortable with an old-fashioned kettle, on a gas hob. There was actually a picture of a lit gas hob. This seemed poor advice to give to the family of a patient who had reduced short-term memory. I couldn't begin to count the number of times I had boiled and reboiled the electric kettle, forgetting that I was going to make a cup of tea, because I had been distracted by some other task. Later

I would find the teabag in the mug, the kettle lukewarm and remember that I had intended to make myself a drink. Perhaps the idea was that the old-fashioned kettle would make a whistling sound when it boiled. Perhaps an electric kettle with an integral whistle in addition to the automatic off switch could be invented to circumvent this problem.

I didn't have a problem with the fact that the government was trying to raise awareness of dementia, but the process seemed to be a tick-box one. In this, it resembled the four-hour emergency target, which had shown little evidence of effectiveness. On one occasion, when I visited the unit for treatment with the infusion, I was asked to complete my 'dementia training' online (another tick-box exercise). At the time, I was on sick leave and acutely aware of my own cognitive impairment. I remember feeling irritated and upset by such a demand. I was also fearful that I might not pass the test, which involved reading information about dementia on the screen and then remembering the facts to answer a series of multiple-choice questions at the end. It took place in the doctors' office in front of all my colleagues and the junior doctors, who, until my illness, I had been training. One of them had a sixth sense for detecting unease and quietly assisted me.

The quiz was testing my knowledge of dementia services and of how I should not ridicule patients suffering from the condition. There was no information about the fact that a patient with dementia feels bewildered most of the time and does impulsive things because the mechanism to inhibit these reactions has also been impaired. There was no mention of the fluctuating nature of the illness, or the fact that often these patients are driven to keep active in order to feel less agitated and restless. Nor was there any explanation of how aggressive outbursts are part of the condition and that after such an outburst patients are left confused and worried about their abnormal or antisocial reactions. They needed reassurance that they were not at fault. Such feedback would be a kind way to comfort them. I knew this better than most doctors, as in a similar way recently I had been unable to control myself.

Whilst I was quietly cheating at the pointless test in the doctors' office, I was also listening to the background conversation and gentle banter. My colleagues were discussing the merits of drinking alcohol, specifically the benefits of red wine. There had been a recent scientific article on the use of resveratrol to treat patients. I jotted the name 'resveratrol' on my iPhone notes, aware that it wasn't a name I would remember later, and dismissed myself from their company, having completed my mandatory training.

Back home, after the ordeal of the 'dementia quiz', I was feeling more lucid and able to concentrate, although I was still aware that I had difficulties with my short-term memory. By becoming a dementia friend, Anna had unwittingly made me review my own diagnosis. I started searching for and trying to understand numerous diverse articles, not just those related to thiamine deficiency. I concentrated particularly on those pertaining to different types of memory loss. One type was episodic memory loss, which explained the exact symptoms I had: difficulty remembering personal events. I had struggled even to recall the events themselves, let alone the details. I could not actually bring to mind the event of having breakfast earlier in the day and had no recollection of what I had eaten. Yet I was able to recount memories from long ago.

What was scary was that this episodic memory loss was known to occur in patients with thiamine deficiency and also occurred in Alzheimer's dementia. I hoped that my recent episodic memory loss was improving . . . or was it? I had developed a rigid daily routine, having the same meal and insisting on doing the same things at the same time each day. It was rather like wrapping myself in a security blanket. I had porridge for breakfast, a banana mid-morning, nuts to snack on in between and a salad for lunch. There was very little variation from day to day. I also knew the types of foods my system could tolerate. I had been taken aback by how poor my recall had been whilst doing the 'dementia quiz'.

If I'm honest, I had known for some time that my symptoms were suggestive of a dementia diagnosis. I suspect Anna had too. According to the latest government statement on recognising the signs, I noted that I had experienced all of the symptoms described. In addition to struggling to remember recent events, I had problems following conversations, I was forgetting the names of friends and objects, I was repeating myself and having problems with thinking and reasoning, as well as experiencing feelings of confusion, even when I was in familiar places. The difficulty I had experienced recognising routes when driving – visuospatial disorientation – is a key marker of dementia. From my reading, I had been troubled by more than just mild cognitive impairment, which is when the sufferer notices cognitive changes, but these are not enough to interfere with daily life. I had dementia, I was certain, but it was probably at the early stages: mild memory loss, repeating questions, depression and apathy, mood swings, mild language problems and a failing sense of direction. Worryingly, there were some aspects which were consistent with more advanced stages, such as the coordination problems and persistent memory loss.

Although my symptoms were strongly suggestive of a clinical diagnosis of dementia, these symptoms had been partially reversed. I wasn't sure whether they would be fully reversible. I didn't know at what stage dementia becomes irreversible. Is it dependent on the progress? Often slowly progressive diseases are irreversible and acute illnesses completely resolve. This may just be because the chronic illnesses are picked up at a later stage in the natural progression. It could be that dementia at a younger age is more readily treatable. Perhaps regeneration occurs more readily under fifty compared to over eighty years of age. I was really hoping that with more treatment I would be cured. At the same time, I was terrified that I would be unable to function independently by the time I was 50.

The first recorded case of 'presenile dementia' was in a lady called Auguste Deter, who died in 1906 at the age of just 55. Alois Alzheimer had observed her in a Frankfurt asylum, where he recorded that she had a loss of short-term memory, difficulty sleeping and was screaming in the middle of the night in desperation.

'I do not cut myself,' she had cried out repeatedly.

This could have been me, given a few more years of illness and no effective treatment. It could have been me resisting harming myself. It could have been me saying, *'I won't do it!'*

I was worried about the symptoms I had suffered already. Auguste Deter may have had an underlying genetic defect, as she suffered with the disease at such a young age. Some of the cases of early onset dementia are thought to be hereditary. However, genetics are unlikely to explain the dramatic rise in cases seen in today's world. An understanding of the genetic control might help us to elucidate the underlying mechanisms, but dementia has to be due to our lifestyle changes. I began to consider that I might not be quite so special after all!

It was whilst mulling over my background reading that I recognised that I was not the only person in the universe affected in this way. The Lakhani paper, which had proven that thiamine deficiency was treatable with antibiotics and was therefore probably a result of bacterial overgrowth in the gut, had clearly shown there were other patients with the same biochemical problems. In fact, dementia affects one in six people over the age of 80. There are an increasing number of personal accounts, as well as medical literature, showing that cognitive impairment is a common problem and the numbers affected are escalating. If I had demonstrated a reversibility of *my* dementing process, then there was a strong likelihood that other patients with dementia could also be treated in a similar way, at least using the same principles.

For me, it had almost become a game of roulette, with the highest of stakes: my health, my cognitive function – my self-preservation. I spun the wheel, seeking evidence to support my hypothesis, and once more the ball rolled into place. It always did. All the jigsaw pieces were slotting into position. I acknowledged that it wasn't the most scientific way of conducting independent research and I was aware too that I was strongly biased into believing that I was right. But if I was right then I would get better. I *had* to believe that.

I knew that memory loss in Korsakoff's syndrome in alcoholics is associated causally with thiamine deficiency. I wondered whether anyone had looked for the same deficiency in Alzheimer's dementia patients. I was becoming increasingly confident each time I searched for thiamine deficiency and associated disease that I would find the evidence and, predictably, I was proving to be right. In postmortem studies of the brains of patients who died of Alzheimer's disease, thiamine diphosphate (thiamine pyrophosphate – TPP) levels are reduced.[41] TPP is the essential cofactor for all the important cellular reactions. I knew that this would be the finding even before I read the papers. Patients had been administered high-dose oral thiamine (3-8g per day)[42, 43] and, as I suspected, and had personally experienced, this had only been mildly effective or had resulted in no significant improvement. These patients weren't able to absorb oral thiamine either.

I wasn't only interested in Alzheimer's disease, I wondered whether my hunch would explain other neurodegenerative conditions, such as Parkinson's disease. Patients with Parkinson's disease often develop cognitive impairment. Parkinson's disease is associated with restless legs syndrome, diabetes[44] and with low plasma thiamine levels. Genetic studies have even identified factors that link thiamine to Parkinson's disease pathology.[45, 46] The same group who treated patients suffering from fibromyalgia with intravenous thiamine also treated patients with Parkinson's disease, finding that high-dose intravenous thiamine led to a dramatic improvement in the patients' ability to move.[47] This time, the study included three patients: n=3. This wasn't the only case report. Intravenous thiamine had been used by another group and had resulted in some patients being able to stop their medication. Thiamine treatment that bypasses the gut seemed to be effective.

I found the name I had jotted down in the office: 'Resveratrol'. That night, my bedtime reading was all about the chemicals in red wine. Red wine is known to be beneficial, but why?

Resveratrol

I HAD FOUND A WAY TO INCREASE MY thiamine levels. After investigating fat-soluble thiamine products, I'd ordered a bulk load of benfotiamine off the internet. According to blog sites, this was the product diabetics were using to combat peripheral neuropathy. It had been around for decades and was even found in small amounts in roasted garlic. Originally used in Japan, it seemed it was now available worldwide, but as a food product and not as a prescription drug. I discovered that even the FDA had recognised that it probably wasn't harmful – or was generally regarded as safe (GRAS). I thought how great it would be if I could control the harmful effects of bacterial overgrowth without antibiotics, just by using benfotiamine.

I set myself a new mini project to investigate the role of diet and small intestinal bacterial overgrowth. It seemed a topical issue and it would be good to see if my hypothesis, that thiamine deficiency due to thiamine breakdown by abnormal or excess intestinal bacteria exacerbated by other factors, e.g. diet, stasis, could explain some of what is known about common diseases.

Following on from the office banter I had overheard, I started with red wine – not drinking it myself, though, as alcohol is a neurotoxin.

'Ye canna drink agin!' Fraser had told me, in his direct manner. I knew he was right.

Moderate wine drinkers reportedly have a lower risk of all cause mortality and cardiovascular disease.[48] They also have a lower incidence of cognitive dysfunction[49] and neurodegenerative diseases such as Alzheimer's[50] and Parkinson's disease.[51] This did not come as a surprise to me, but secretly I was rather pleased with myself when I discovered that there were published articles showing that red wine can act as an antibiotic.[52] The antimicrobial effect of the beverage is actually well documented, and is partly due to plant phenols, especially resveratrol.[53] It turns out that resveratrol, found in grape skin, is produced as part of the grape's natural defence mechanism against bacterial or fungal infections.[54] In fact, it is well understood that resveratrol has antimicrobial properties.

There were lots of papers. Flicking through them, I could see resveratrol had beneficial effects in alcoholic liver disease in mice[55], and in mild encephalopathy[56], the confusion seen in patients with advanced liver disease – this condition is now predominantly treated with the antibiotic rifaximin. I was keen to discover if there was any other link with diet and small intestinal bacterial overgrowth, irritable bowel disease or diabetes. I found a paper showing that in rats fed a high fructose diet, the subsequent metabolic syndrome was ameliorated by resveratrol.[57] Resveratrol also improved non-alcoholic fatty liver in rats that developed obesity and insulin resistance (metabolic syndrome) after being fed a high-fat diet. The investigators detected the activation of a specific enzyme involved in glucose and fat metabolism – AMP-activated protein kinase, which requires phosphorylation for activation.[58] Interestingly, this enzyme is inhibited in thiamine deficiency.[59] At least this topic would interest Matthew and may even pass the breakfast table test.

On further reading, I was delighted to discover that by reducing dietary carbohydrate it is possible to change gut bacterial flora. More specifically, it actually alters the activity of the thiamine-dependent enzymes.[60] Transferring bacteria from the intestines of malnourished children to mice, and then feeding the mice a high-carbohydrate diet, results in them becoming malnourished. The same mice given a high-protein diet do not become malnourished. The malnourished mice have reduced activity of the Kreb's cycle, the series of enzyme reactions that are predominantly dependent on thiamine.[61] It seems that a high-carbohydrate diet alters the gut bacteria, which seems to affect the thiamine-dependent pathways.

A diet with increased protein and fat and reduced carbohydrate is effective at reducing insulin levels and improving glycaemic control in diabetic patients with metabolic syndrome.[62, 63] In non-alcoholic fatty liver disease, a high-carbohydrate diet is associated with increased inflammation, whilst a high-fat diet is associated with lower levels of inflammation.[64] Patients with irritable bowel syndrome also respond to a low-carbohydrate diet.

I moved onto reading about the popular diets: Mediterranean, Atkins, 5:2 and South Beach. These diets all recommend increased fruit and vegetable intake, reduced carbohydrate consumption or periods of fasting. Therefore, each diet reduces bacterial load by either reducing the substrate for bacteria (recommending low-carbohydrate or fasting), or by increasing the natural antimicrobial content of the diet (increasing fruit and vegetables).

I referred to my favourite scientist, Yudkin, whose book, *Pure, White and Deadly: How Sugar is Killing Us and What We Can Do to Stop It*, had just been rereleased. Originally it was published in 1972, but the new version had an introduction by the paediatric endocrinologist Dr Robert Lustig. Fraser recommended I buy a copy. He believed my hypothesis and had completely changed his diet. He no longer bought packets of biscuits and jelly babies for the office. His children were on a strict, reduced-sugar diet. He was horrified by how much sugar was contained in even the 'healthy' cereals, just to make the taste appeal to children. In Yudkin's book, there were accounts of his research, and I was impelled to look up his original papers.[65] He had conducted a series of experiments in thiamine-deficient rats and found that they could thrive despite thiamine deficiency, provided their diet was free from sucrose. He proposed that the effects of thiamine deficiency were due to the body trying to breakdown dietary carbohydrate with insufficient thiamine. He thought this produced toxins, and he described it as metabolic processes that had been 'perverted', explaining that it was effectively the incomplete breakdown of sugars that caused the problem. Thiamine deficiency without sugar is tolerated. Just as, in a similar way, cortisol deficiency with salt is tolerated in the absence of infection.

Without realising it, Yudkin had identified the underlying cause of metabolic syndrome (and named it appropriately as an abnormal metabolism). He explained metabolic syndrome as a state that wasn't due to thiamine deficiency per se, but was the body's attempt to manage excess carbohydrate (and therefore sugar) when the thiamine-dependent pathways required for the detoxification of sugar were inactivated because of thiamine deficiency.

Applying Yudkin's theory to the seesaw diagrams:

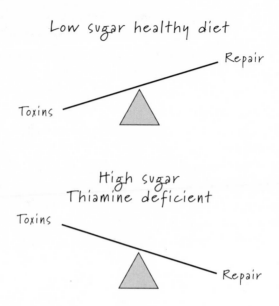

We currently recognise that excess sugar is a problem. We also understand that exercise is largely beneficial, as it burns up excess calories. Unfortunately, exercise requires energy and energy release from food is significantly reduced by thiamine deficiency. Yudkin had shown that the underlying problem is excess sugar in the presence of thiamine deficiency. In time, though, this crucial fact had been overlooked. There could be no doubt that thiamine was the missing link.

Metabolic syndrome is simply due to an imbalance between sugar and thiamine. Perhaps this explained why I had escaped the full-blown picture of metabolic syndrome. I realised that I had been thiamine deficient, and although I had briefly increased my sugar intake for a few months, which was when it was noticed that I had cholesterol deposits in my eyes, I now had virtually no sugar in my diet. I had also reduced my carbohydrate intake. The cholesterol deposits were evidence that I was developing microvascular disease. The metabolic syndrome required the lethal combination of sugar excess and low thiamine to occur.

There was no getting away from the puzzle; there were pieces of the jigsaw everywhere I looked – newspapers, magazines, journals and the radio:

'Sugar is as bad as alcohol.'

The British Medical Journal ran a series on sugar[66-68], written by doctors from many medical disciplines. The message was clear: sugar is bad for us, not fat. Scientists had finally recognised the dangers of sugar; sugary drinks were causing obesity.

There were other articles that made sense, knowing what I now knew about the symptoms. I was really enjoying myself once more. Solving this riddle was giving me a sense of achievement similar to the sense of satisfaction some people derive from completing a particularly difficult Sudoku. I tested each snippet of information to see if it fitted.

A lunchtime lecture on the subject of dementia was being held in the hospital. The audience, mostly made up of research nurses, chortled as the lecturer put up a picture of someone brushing their teeth. They belittled the research that had apparently demonstrated how keeping your teeth clean could reduce dementia. I could tell that they were thinking: *How could something as simple as mouth care reduce such a complex disease as dementia? What a ridiculous notion!* I didn't think so. Dental hygiene had been something that had interested me for a while. The patients with the worst prognosis in the hospital seemed to have the worst teeth and gums. I had even been accused of not brushing my teeth. I was horrified to think that my gums were receding. When I had been ill, plaque developed rapidly and my oral hygiene seemed poor. On regular antibiotics this had not been a problem, particularly when I chewed them!

I was curious to know why this was, and why brushing your teeth should help reduce dementia. I pondered whilst sitting in the auditorium. I was determined to solve this new part of the riddle.

It didn't take long to think of a plausible rationale. If you can reduce the number of bacteria in your mouth, which is supposed to contain more bacteria than the average toilet bowl (obviously not a breakfast table topic), then it follows that this will reduce the number of bacteria in your intestines.

Scientists conducting the early studies on small intestinal bacterial overgrowth had been puzzled by the results. The bacteria detected in the small intestines had been similar to those in the mouth. They had assumed that the probe used to sample the intestinal contents had simply picked up the oral flora as it had passed through the mouth, contaminating the catheter. The results were interpreted as spurious and of dubious significance, and the bacteria found were not thought to be a true representation of the bacteria in the small gut.

I questioned whether this was so. Perhaps the bacteria you are most likely to get in the gut are the ones from the oral cavity. I thought it much more likely that most of the bacteria in the small intestines would be taken in orally, rather than swim like eels from the nether regions. What if the dementia research was correct and brushing your teeth actually helped to reduce the bacterial burden on the gut? Oral hygiene was, therefore, important for dementia prevention.

The next session in the lecture was a bid to become the lead in a multicentre research trial looking at the effect of using omega-3 fish oil to reduce dementia by giving patients fish to eat thrice weekly. There seemed to be no control for the amount of sugar ingested on this fish diet. I couldn't recall any studies suggesting that eating fish altered the microbiome in the gut. It seemed as though they were missing the point.

That evening, I read that other factors increased the number of bacteria in the small intestines, including proton pump inhibitors (PPI). PPI are a class of drugs, which, by reducing the acid production in the stomach, encourage stomach ulcers to heal. Ulcers do not occur without acid. However, ulcers or inflammation also occur if there is infection (Helicobacter pylori), and with drugs such as aspirin-like medicines and alcohol. PPI can reduce the associated inflammation and are therefore frequently used. However, there are good reasons why the stomach produces acid – it helps with digestion and defends against bacteria. By neutralising stomach acid, the guts become open to attack. No one doubts that PPIs have had a tremendous effect on reducing mortality from bleeding ulcers – eradicating Helicobacter pylori – and even in protecting against chemical insult from aspirin, but these widely prescribed drugs certainly alter the gut microbiome (bacterial flora). Surely this is having a deleterious effect? To my satisfaction, there were studies showing that small intestinal bacterial overgrowth was indeed more common in patients taking PPI.[34] It seemed there were growing concerns that PPI use could lead to dementia.[69] What then followed was a large number of articles and further research counteracting the original study, with media reports that PPI were safe, so the public were left confused. Does this sound familiar? PPI use is also linked to a greater risk of fracture.[70] I presume this is due to long-term vitamin D malabsorption.

I was also concerned about drugs that have an adverse effect on the autonomic nervous system. It always saddened me to see patients with serious mental health problems taking major antipsychotics, as the side-effect profile of these medicines is horrific. Antipsychotics cause dry mouth, constipation and visual disturbance, as they mess up all the housekeeping functions. The reason for this is that many of these drugs have anticholinergic effects. By blocking the neurotransmitter acetylcholine they effectively cause autonomic nerve dysfunction. (Acetylcholine is the neurotransmitter that the dementia drugs, the anticholinesterases, aim to increase. Isn't modern medicine marvellous?) Many patients eventually become cognitively impaired, to add to their mental health issues. I strongly suspect that these medicines help to promote bacterial overgrowth by causing gut stasis, thus leading to thiamine depletion. In the gastroenterology clinic, I had seen patients with mental health issues displaying symptoms of thiamine deficiency (although I didn't see the link at the time), particularly cognitive impairment and lack of coordination. In addition, they were often overweight and/or suffering terribly from constipation. I now understood the underlying problem. If only I could have prescribed benfotiamine. Would it have worked, I wonder? It probably should be started at the same time as antipsychotics, in order to prevent deteriorating cognitive function. It is possible that any underlying mental illness is due to thiamine deficiency, or at least exacerbated by it, so perhaps antipsychotics aren't even necessary in some cases. What is required is the treatment of poor nutrition. Instead, we as doctors go against the cardinal rule of medicine, 'First, do no harm.'

The British Medical Journal was delivered to our house each week. Initially, I would glance through the obituaries and then go onto Minerva – the section on the last page, which has an overview of the news from other journals. One morning, an article caught my attention. It was a study linking benzodiazepine use to a 50% increased risk of dementia.[71]

For once, I had Matthew's attention at the breakfast table. He even put down his toast to wait for an explanation. Benzodiazepines are a class of drugs that include some sleeping tablets, for example, Valium. They also have an anti-anxiety effect, and since their synthesis in the 1960s they have been widely prescribed. I tried to think of a reason for the link. They don't have an antimicrobial effect and they don't influence the autonomic nervous system. So, what was the connection?

'Thiamine deficiency causes anxiety and insomnia,' I suggested to Matthew, as, at the same time, I worked through the putative mechanism in my mind. In my case, thiamine deficiency had certainly led to terrific problems with insomnia.

'If the doctor prescribes an anxiolytic, such as a benzodiazepine, to alleviate the symptoms of anxiety and help induce sleep, then it is not too difficult to understand why the use of these drugs is associated with dementia.'

Matthew poured more tea for us both. 'Milk, please,' he said.

'It is merely an association, but not causal,' I concluded, passing the milk and sipping my tea, while I waited for a response. Matthew was now finishing his toast, nodding pensively. 'I might cycle the Loddon Loop this morning,' he said, and I was jolted back to reality. He clearly had other things on his mind.

Pressing on, I also reported to Matthew that benfotiamine, which is converted to thiamine after absorption, had been used successfully in patients with alcohol dependency to reduce the symptoms of alcohol withdrawal, notably psychiatric symptoms, such as obsessive-compulsive traits and anxiety.[72] It was clear why treatment with high dose intravenous thiamine on the ward also helped patients with alcohol dependency, but once they were discharged they often relapsed to their old habits and started drinking again. The standard dose of oral thiamine was 50-100mg, which I now knew was woefully inadequate. I doubted much of this would be absorbed. The patients who were more successful at staving off the alcohol after discharge were the ones who had been severely ill and had almost died. I, like most of the medical profession, had thought it was because they had been frightened into stopping drinking. Perhaps this wasn't the case. During their prolonged stay in hospital, these patients had been treated for longer with higher doses of intravenous thiamine. They'd had time off alcohol to enable their thiamine-uptake transporter, which was inactivated by alcohol use, to recover sufficiently. In addition, they often required antibiotics, which would have altered their gut bacteria.

I checked to see whether there was any potential causal association between benzodiazepines and dementia. Benzodiazepines activate the GABA (gamma-aminobutyric acid) receptors in the brain, triggering a release of the neurotransmitter GABA. GABA is an inhibitory neurotransmitter that makes people feel calm and sleepy. I found an article that showed how the brains of thiamine-deficient rats contained less glutamate and GABA. Glutamate is an excitatory neurotransmitter, thought to have an important role in memory. So did this mean that thiamine deficiency causes glutamate deficiency? With my understanding of the Kreb's cycle, this was certainly feasible. After all, glutamate is synthesised from alpha-ketoglutarate, an intermediate in the biochemical pathway, which is dependent on thiamine. GABA is synthesised from glutamate. Perhaps thiamine deficiency also leads to a deficiency in GABA in humans, which is temporarily alleviated by benzodiazepines, although the underlying problem – thiamine deficiency – is not corrected.

Meanwhile, scientists collaborating on behalf of *The Lancet Commission on Dementia Prevention and Cure* identified nine modifiable risk factors: diabetes, obesity, hypertension, physical inactivity, depression, smoking, hearing loss, low educational attainment and social isolation. They estimated that over a third of the cases of Alzheimer's dementia would be prevented if people heeded lifestyle advice.[73] It is clear that dementia is the metabolic syndrome of the brain; it is linked to diabetes and obesity. In addition, there is a correlation with symptoms characteristic of thiamine deficiency: depression, physical inactivity and social isolation. Preventing dementia by reducing these risk factors: diabetes, obesity, hypertension, physical inactivity, etc., was not going to be that simple. We already know that telling people to exercise more is often unsuccessful. The main problem is that dementia is a syndrome and, as I had already found out, there are no specialists for syndromes.

I was taking 1g of benfotiamine daily. It was fat-soluble so I was able to absorb it more readily, especially as the fat malabsorption associated with bacterial overgrowth had been corrected by rifaximin.

As a result of these treatments, I no longer had anxiety or insomnia. My hands and feet were not painful. I felt hopeful that my cognitive function was improving, too. In fact, the results of an online, number-recall memory test I tried were promising. My short-term memory was reasonable. I felt encouraged. Another few years of my peers drinking and eating too much and I might be on par with them. They might all catch up with me!

Ten Per Cent Human

THE MANAGERS AT WORK LIVED in fear of losing their jobs. A bullying culture had existed in the trust for years. As a consequence of cost cutting, our service was not being developed in line with the expansion of patient numbers. Even so, there had been a dramatic increase in the number of cardiologists and orthopaedic surgeons. There were always new anaesthetic posts to expand Matthew's department. Fraser and I had been in discussion with the divisional general manager about replacing a full-time consultant post, as one of our colleagues had moved to another hospital. We were told that there wasn't enough money in the pot. There wouldn't be enough funds to take on a full-time consultant, even though the colleague who had left had been working full-time and was employed by the trust for many years. I can only assume this money had been redeployed for use elsewhere.

'The problem is, you make a 500% loss,' the manager told us categorically.

Our department was essential to the running of a large emergency teaching hospital. But apparently it was still costing the hospital money! The idea that treating sick patients 'made' money was an anathema. What did he want us to do about it? Close the department? Pull the pin? We already took more than our fair share of the 'business' – it had been a sore point for years.

There were multiple incidences where we had basically done the work for another department. There was the patient with right upper quadrant pain, nausea and vomiting, with fatty intolerance and abnormal liver function – we had to prove he had gallstones before the surgeons would take him over. There was the patient with central abdominal pain, which was localised to the right lower quadrant, who we diagnosed with appendicitis; the patient with shoulder pains two weeks after a shoulder replacement; the ones with haematoma of their knee, unable to mobilise, a week after a knee replacement. These patients somehow defaulted to General Medicine and became our responsibility.

Some of them had postoperative blood clots. I checked on the surgical curriculum and an understanding of the presentation and treatment of blood clots was expected knowledge, as was the management of postoperative complications. On the other side of the coin, an ability to operate on a patient with gallstones or appendicitis was definitely not on *our* curriculum.

Without our department, the hospital would struggle to deal with the increasing number of emergencies. Without emergencies it would become an elective surgical centre, only performing the non-emergency operations. This attitude made no sense. We had to provide cover for the emergency work. I really didn't understand the rationale, except that the turnover of managers was high, higher still than in political parties. Their only role seemed to be to balance the books short-term. There was no apparent interest in patient care.

I primarily kept myself up-to-date by seeing patients. I learnt by reading about interesting cases. This wasn't enough, as I had to maintain my professional development by showing that I was continuing to learn. It was one thing reading about medical cases or all the literature on thiamine, but I couldn't prove anything about my hypothesis and I couldn't demonstrate that I had been reading and 'developing' my knowledge. I thought about writing an article for the *British Medical Journal* entitled 'The Patient's Journey'. I asked Fraser to co-author it, but once it was written I delayed publishing it, until I felt it was too late. The case report lacked any scientific evidence. It was n=1 – an experimental trial of one person. It wasn't going to change anything.

Even so, my understanding of the symptoms of thiamine deficiency had affected the way I treated patients. In contrast, the 'professional development' conferences I attended rarely influenced my clinical practice. Fraser agreed that he had changed his practice too – these days he also treated far more patients with intravenous vitamins. We were both secretly delighted at our multidisciplinary team meeting when the pharmacist questioned why this particular intravenous drug was in the top 10 drugs prescribed on the unit. In fact, it was at number three. Fraser and I felt proud of our achievements. It was childish really, but we seldom felt empowered to change anything. This was different – the drug was cheap, there were almost never any side effects and it wasn't difficult to do; any patient with risk factors for thiamine deficiency was offered treatment with the vitamin infusion. These included those with heavy alcohol intake, excessive weight loss, probable malnutrition, malabsorption and confusion of uncertain cause . . . the list was endless.

Our standard drug chart had heparin – the blood-thinning medicine – printed on the first row, as it was majorly in need. The doctors only had to sign the box to prescribe it. Immobility in hospital is a risk factor for blood clots (deep vein thrombosis), which can be fatal if they travel to the lungs and cause a pulmonary embolism. In my view, it would make just as much sense to have thiamine printed on the second row. In fact, there were probably more patients who would meet the criteria for thiamine-replacement therapy on admission to hospital than heparin, and I was certain there were more who would benefit from treatment.

I admitted a lady in her mid-fifties who was underweight and confessed to drinking excess alcohol and not eating properly (meeting three of our criteria). She was in a hysterical state (possibly a fourth), and had clearly been crying. She had mascara in streaks across her cheeks and a mottled, swollen face from the combination of tears, anger and the typical round facial appearance of parotid (cheek) gland enlargement seen in malnourished alcoholics. She had been in trouble with the police and was distraught because she could not explain her aggressive outburst. Although she had not been held in custody, she was distressed because she had overreacted. I explained that I understood how she was feeling and said that I may be able to treat her.

Instantly, the patient turned away from me, her hostile posture making it clear that my attentions were not welcome. From experience, I knew that such patients are the very ones who would most benefit from having someone show an interest in them. Calmly and kindly, I tried again. I was all too aware that this technique does not always work. In the past, I had been at the receiving end of a sharp slap to the face, a punch to the body, and been spat at. I had already established that this patient had consumed a poor diet for months or years, and that recently she had lost even more weight. I was sure there were other issues, too, but the patient wasn't prepared to trust me or discuss them behind the paper-thin curtains separating her bed space from that of the next patient. Of one thing I was sure – this patient had multiple risk factors for thiamine deficiency and also had symptoms consistent with it.

She reluctantly agreed to an infusion of vitamins, which included intravenous thiamine, although I could tell that she really didn't believe it would help. I half expected her to sign herself out during the night. The next morning, the duty nurse caught me by the arm. Immediately I thought that I was about to be scolded for keeping the woman in overnight. I waited to hear a detailed account of how disruptive the patient had been, but instead the nurse told me that she wanted to see me. I figured this could be an interesting meeting. I felt sure the woman would berate me for giving her false hope, and I regretted being quite so sure I could alleviate all her troubles.

When I went to see her, she was sitting on the edge of her bed, freshly showered, dressed and packed, her back towards me. As I approached the bed, she turned around and stood up, before spontaneously hugging me. She explained that she now felt calm and rested; she had slept well on the ward and realised that she had not been acting rationally the day before. She was 'cured'. It reminded me of the incredible feeling I had experienced after my first vitamin infusion. I was pleased I was able to help her in a small way, but recognised that any help would be short lived. I doubted she would purchase thiamine, or better still, benfotiamine tablets. I knew that benfotiamine had been used to treat the mental health problems associated with alcohol use, and that the patients with mental illnesses most likely have thiamine deficiency.[72] Would she stop drinking long enough for thiamine to be effective? It may already be too late and the thiamine alone may not be absorbed. Even if she obtained some benfotiamine, would she take it regularly?

Another lady I saw in clinic had terrible problems with slow transit through her bowels. She had lost a significant amount of weight through diet and exercise. And although she had been intensively investigated, no cause was found. The exercising was out of hand; she would power walk all day, every day. I'd frequently seen her almost running through town. I explained my hypothesis about thiamine being used up by overexertion. I also recommended thiamine replacement and told her that diabetic patients were using benfotiamine, as it was better absorbed. I felt sure that she had gut stasis; on an X-ray, the dilated loops of bowel were obvious. She was willing to try anything, but told me that benfotiamine was too expensive. I was disappointed, as I was powerless to help her – I could not prescribe it and she could not afford it. It was no better than needing expensive cortisol injections in the 1930s, pre-NHS. I flippantly mentioned that it was cheaper to buy thiamine for horses – irritated that horse owners could afford these medicines while my patients could not.

I had to attend some meetings, so that I could file a certificate of attendance in my portfolio. I looked specifically for ones on small intestinal bacterial overgrowth, and although I had missed a few in the States, there were none in Britain. The agenda for dementia conferences tended to focus on caring for patients rather than preventing and treating the disease, and any talks on the gut-brain axis or neuro-gastro-motility were across the Atlantic. The meeting nearest to my interests, both clinically and geographically, was a liver disease symposium in Cambridge. I had been a regular attendee earlier in my career, when I had hankered after a liver job. I remember sitting in the back row of the lecture theatre back then whilst breastfeeding Emily. The organiser had been positive about me taking my baby daughter along, and I was keen to change archaic attitudes. I wasn't quite so confident that I was doing the right thing as Emily slurped, burped and noisily filled her nappy throughout the talk. For this meeting, in the very same auditorium, I arrived early and sat in the middle. Then Richard entered, came down the steps and sat next to me. I hadn't seen him since his cynical 'Nobel Prize' remark.

The first speaker talked about the microbiome (the bacteria in the gut). 'We are only 10% human,' he announced, as he showed his first slide. 'We are more bacteria than human in terms of the number of cells.'

Richard was engrossed in the scientific presentation, fidgeting and biting his nails. The next speaker talked about a medication called 'urso deoxycholic acid', which, because of its anti-inflammatory actions, had been used for treating liver disease for years. It was identical chemically to the substance found in polar bear bile acid. Richard bounced his leg up and down against the seat, which he always did when he was excited by something, and leaned towards me. 'It alters the gut bacteria,' he whispered, 'we now know that's how it works.'

I smiled. He acted as though he was sharing a big secret. He seemed to have completely forgotten our meeting, my hypothesis and his reaction.

I wanted to know whether this drug improved vitamin D levels, as a marker of its effect on gut bacteria. I didn't think there would be any point looking up the drug 'ursodeoxycholic acid' and 'thiamine', as there would almost certainly be no research – no one measured thiamine levels any more. Vitamin D levels were often measured and seemed a reasonable surrogate marker for bacterial overgrowth. I would have to wait until I was back home to look it up.

When I searched for the effect of this drug on vitamin D, I realised it was more complicated than I'd imagined. Ursodeoxycholic acid was originally used for the medical treatment of gallstones. The bears produced this chemical constituent of bile so that they could hibernate without developing gallstones. Natural bile salts and treatments like ursodeoxycholic acid stimulate the production of a protein called cathelicidin[74], which has antibacterial and antiviral properties. So presumably, this is how it impacts the microbiome.

Vitamin D also increases the amount of cathelicidin that is produced.[74] Mucus membranes, including the skin and the respiratory and gastrointestinal tracts, produce cathelicidin – a natural antimicrobial agent. It was no wonder I had problems with recurrent skin infections, viral infections and diarrhoeal illnesses when I was severely vitamin D deficient. It probably explains the population's tendency to develop seasonal flu and cold symptoms, as vitamin D levels are always lower in the winter months. Acne is also thought to be worse during the colder seasons. Vitamin D is produced in the skin in response to ultraviolet light, or sunlight, which is significantly reduced in the Northern Hemisphere from October to March.

Polar bear bile acid promoted this antibacterial agent. Vitamin D also increased it. Reducing gut bacteria increases vitamin D. In reverse it was a vicious circle. We had unwittingly been using an antibacterial agent on liver disease patients.

Although interesting and no doubt linked to thiamine deficiency, I needed to refocus on thiamine. I decided to find out as much as possible about its breakdown and, more specifically, the mechanisms involved.

★

I was walking through town when I recognised my patient from clinic powerwalking towards me. She waved exuberantly, clearly delighted to see me. She obviously hadn't got the message about overdoing it, but she was pleased to tell me she had bought horse thiamine online and it had worked brilliantly!

Thiaminases

IT SEEMED THAT IN CERTAIN CIRCLES the enzymatic destruction of thiamine was well known. Cat lovers and garter snake owners all seemed to be aware of it. In fact, pets the world over were protected by their owners from the effects of thiamine deficiency. Plenty of information was available on the internet and people were exchanging tales and giving advice – recommending the avoidance of giving certain types of raw fish to their beloved pets. The feeding of raw carp had also led to severe thiamine deficiency in foxes.[75] This thiamine-destroying enzyme was called thiaminase.

I latched onto the fact that thiaminase could potentially be important. Thiaminase had caused mass mortality in the salmon industry.[76] There were articles on thiaminase being found in herrings from the Baltic Sea.[77] I wondered if this was when my slow deterioration had started. Living in Holland, I'd eaten many pickled, raw herrings. I'd been pregnant again, the third pregnancy in almost as many years, and I remembered feeling exhausted, emotional and irrational. Of course, I'd put that down to pregnancy and hormones. Postpartum, I had felt shooting pains in my arms. I rationalised these were due to breastfeeding in an awkward position, even though I had not suffered with them while nursing my other two.

There were several publications about thiaminases dating from the 1970s and concerning diseases in sheep (polioencephalomalacia).[78] I came across papers describing cerebrocortical necrosis (literally brain rot) caused by thiaminase-induced thiamine deficiency – a similar condition is found in ruminants (animals that ferment plant-based food in specially adapted stomachs prior to digestion), such as cattle.[79] It seemed thiamine deficiency in these animals was possibly associated with them eating horsetail fern (equisetum), a type of plant, which contains thiaminase. Other plants were also poisonous, including bracken.[80] Not all cases were clear-cut, however, although it was the young animals, lambs in this case, that were most susceptible.

It was suggested that excessive sulphur might also be associated with thiamine deficiency. Sulphur dioxide is used to prevent discolouration and as a preservative in the meat industry. In the past, there had been several cases of thiamine deficiency in dogs and cats fed fresh meat (instead of cheaper, tinned food) treated with the preservative.[81] It seems that sulphur dioxide inactivates thiamine. Sulphur dioxide is found in significant amounts in sausages and preserved meats, such as salamis. It is added to extend the shelf life and prevent the growth of other harmful bacteria, such as salmonella and clostridia. Ruminants also developed pathological lesions similar to thiamine deficiency if they were exposed to high sulphur, either in feed, supplements, or if the environment contained a high amount of hydrogen sulphide.[82]

There was a really helpful page on the regularly updated Cornell University website, which explained all about thiaminases in great detail. It described the two types, thiaminase I and II, and how they differed. In addition, I read about the Australian explorers who had died after eating Nardoo water fern. The Aborigines ate this all the time and suffered no ill effects, whereas the travellers described how they had become weaker and weaker.[83] It transpired that they had not understood how to prepare it properly. Nardoo fern contains thiaminases. Soaking and cooking the plant in a certain way destroys this, making it safe to eat.

In my search for evidence of thiaminase, I found reports of a seasonal ataxia due to thiamine deficiency in African people who ate silkworm pupae.[84] African land snails also contained thiaminase and were consumed as a source of protein.[85] It was curious that molluscs and young insects should also contain it. I also happened to find a series of papers from 1948 entitled 'Technological studies of the starfish.' One of the papers reported on the abundance of starfish and an unsuccessful trial to use it in animal feed. The animals all developed thiamine deficiency. Starfish contain thiaminase.[86] The paper explained that a chemical in fish that destroyed thiamine was known about as early as 1941, and at that time most thiaminase had been found in aquatic animals.

I read about some researchers from Japan who, in the 1950s, fed a species of bacteria – *Bacillus thiaminolyticus* – to animals, including cats, chickens, guinea pigs and rats. Within days they had found the enzyme thiaminase in the animals' faeces and noted that they displayed signs of thiamine deficiency, mainly poor appetite and weakness. Confusingly, some animals remained carriers without developing symptoms.[87] Hence, the thiaminase enzyme is produced by certain species of bacteria; it is an exoenzyme[88], which means that it is secreted to work outside the organism. It is also remarkably stable and passes through the gut unchanged. I was surprised to find that thiaminase had even been found in human faeces. This paper, dated from 1981, was written by a researcher called Duffy[89], who had found that approximately 20% of the Melanesian people were thiamine deficient. Thiaminase was present in 50% of the stool samples tested. It was thought to be of bacterial origin. I looked up more about Duffy to see if he had conducted any other experiments, but nothing came of the search. Giving up on him, I then tried to find out more about Melanesia.

Melanesia, a region in the Pacific Ocean off the northeast coast of Australia, consists of countries such as Papua New Guinea, Fiji and the Solomon Islands. I didn't know much about Papua New Guinea, except that in the past they had practised cannibalism. What interested me was a WHO report on the incidence of obesity in the population of these islands – 50-90% of the residents were reported to be overweight. Apparently, the prevalence of diabetes in adults in the Pacific region is among the highest in the world, and 40% of the population has cardiovascular disease, diabetes and hypertension – the metabolic syndrome.

In 1954, in Guy's Hospital, London, a couple of microbiologists called Citron and Knox[90] provided yet more evidence to support the link between bacterial overgrowth and thiamine deficiency. Their paper reported a case of a 75-year-old man who had developed a dysfunction of multiple nerves throughout his body (polyneuritis). His symptoms sounded rather like an attack of beriberi. Unfortunately, he had suffered for six years and then died. There was some suggestion clinically that he may have had malabsorption. Postmortem samples of his gut revealed *Staphylococcus aureus*, among other bacteria. There is a lot of bad publicity about *Staphylococcus aureus*, although most people will recognise it as the 'killer bug' or MRSA, rather than by its formal Latin name.

When growing the *S. aureus* in laboratory conditions, in the presence of glucose and thiamine, the thiamine vanished from the surrounding liquid. The disappearance of thiamine was much greater with *S. aureus* compared with the other bacteria such as *E. Coli* and *Proteus*, although it was still a feature with these. It was known that yeast destroyed the thiamine, but in this experiment it was felt that the thiamine was simply taken up by the bacteria. When the bacteria were destroyed, the thiamine seemed to reappear. These microbiologists hypothesised that the bacteria caused the thiamine deficiency in the patient. They made the assumption that infection in the gut would render the patient thiamine deficient, as thiamine would not be available for absorption.

More recent research has shown that the enzyme thiaminase II, also known as 'Ten A protein', has been found in *S. aureus*[91], mentioned in the aforementioned case. Presumably, this was responsible for the disappearing thiamine. This thiaminase enzyme, Ten A, is also produced by the spore-producing bacteria *Bacillus subtilis*[92], which is widely found in soil, as well as by yeast, *Saccharomyces cerevisiae*.[93]

The Cornell webpage once again helped me to understand all about thiaminase II. The main difference between the two enzymes, thiaminase I and thiaminase II, is the position at which thiamine is broken – the cleavage site.

Thiamine consists of two compounds linked together, a 6-carbon pyrimidine ring (represented by the hexagon, over the page) and a 5-carbon ring thiazole portion containing sulphur (represented by the pentagon). In the schematic diagram over the page, each corner and turn, and even the ends of the lines, represent a hydrocarbon group.

Pyrimidine ring

Thiazole

Thiaminase I cleaves the thiamine in two and then exchanges the thiazole for another substance.

Ten A, or thiaminase II, cleaves the thiamine into the constituent compounds: pyrimidine and thiazole, reacting with water to replace the thiazole with hydroxide (OH). In fact, it produces a specific pyrimidine compound called 4-amino-5-hydroxymethyl-2-methylpyrimidine (HMP), where methyl is the CH3 hydrocarbon group. The 4, 5 and 2 simply denote which groups are attached to which carbons in the ring. This compound is a known substrate for thiamine synthesis.

Therefore, the thiamine is rendered inactive to humans by these enzymes. With the right enzymes, the constituents can be resynthesised into whole thiamine. Mammals do not have these enzymes and are not able to resynthesise thiamine, thus becoming thiamine deficient. Conversely, bacteria can resynthesise thiamine.

Picture sad, wasted, thiamine-deficient humans and happy bacteria, full of thiamine.

I tried to discover more about thiaminase and the reason bacteria have developed to use it. I started reading about the ecological interactions of thiamine.[94] By this stage, I had worked out that thiamine status in humans is fragile. I also agreed with the authors who thought that thiamine had received little attention in recent years. What was alarming was the scarcity of this vitamin – free thiamine is present in water in the tiniest amounts. Hence, thiamine and the thiamine substrates have to be efficiently recycled. This is what bacteria and marine animals are doing – they are salvaging thiamine and thiamine breakdown products and resynthesising thiamine for their own use. It's very clever. Alas, humans have a design glitch, a flaw, which has been uncovered by a diet consisting of excess sugar and a genetic makeup that hasn't evolved to cope.

It transpired that the researchers Citron and Knox had been correct; thiamine was present in *S. aureus,* having been resynthesised by the specialist bacterial enzymes.

It is thought that this is the purpose of both thiaminase I[95] and thiaminase II – salvaging thiamine precursors. Production of these enzymes, therefore, confers a survival advantage. Throughout the living kingdom there is marked diversity in the ability of creatures to produce, degrade and hoard components of thiamine. In terms of 'survival of the fittest', this confers a strong selection advantage to anything living that can obtain this vitamin. Horsetail fossils have shown us that this plant has survived for millions of years, and it is probably the 'oldest' plant on earth. It's interesting that horsetail has made use of salvaging thiamine.

Thinking about the case of polyneuritis, I wasn't really aware of people getting *S. aureus* in their guts. After all, it was a skin bug, which some patients carried in their nose, groin or axilla. This was standard teaching and is the reason why patients have swabs taken of these areas upon their arrival in hospital. It has been demonstrated that in 20% of patients there is intestinal carriage of *S. aureus*, and in 9% of healthy people the multiresistant variant, MRSA, has been detected.[96] Hence, the intestines are frequently colonised by a bacteria known to be capable of producing thiaminase. I had many more questions to ask. Was the *S. aureus* in the small intestines in these patients, where it could interfere with thiamine absorption? Was there any association with diabetes, hypertension, cardiovascular disease, the metabolic syndrome, or even dementia?

I thought I had read somewhere about a marked increase in the occurrence of Parkinson's disease in hospital workers. I found what I was looking for on a patient information site. A Canadian study had found a greater prevalence of Parkinson's disease in healthcare workers, teachers and people living in close proximity to each other and in crowded conditions. Staphylococcus can certainly travel easily between people in these conditions, particularly in the absence of good hygiene practices, for example hand washing.

I reflected how my father might well have been partly right when he had claimed that infectious microorganisms would 'take over' the world. He had thought that the main threat would be from viruses. However, my take on it was that bacteria may be responsible for extinguishing the human race. Humans thought they were clever in producing antibiotics, but not only are the bacteria developing ways around these medicines (resistance), they are also producing antihuman factors, in the form of thiaminases. A hundred years ago, couples produced many children, women regularly died in childbirth and young children and adults lost their lives to infectious diseases. In the future, if fertility is compromised; if people choose to limit family size because of the burden of looking after their ageing, dependent parents; if the parents living longer are of unsound mind, but strong in body, then population numbers may fall.

I had to admit that I was probably over-dramatising the situation, as currently the population is showing no sign of falling and many of the world's problems seem to be due to overcrowding and the consequent ease of bacterial spread. The WHO had described cardiovascular diseases, diabetes and hypertension as non-communicative diseases, but I was beginning to wonder if this was an oversimplification. There was increasing evidence to suggest that metabolic syndrome and dementia could be a transmissible condition, and one that was certainly more infectious than HIV.

Mark in the Sand

OVER COFFEE ONE DAY IN THE DOCTORS' office, I confided in Nick about an article I'd been working on and my plans to get it published in a leading medical journal.

'Mine was rejected in less time than it took me to finish clinic,' Nick told me, shuffling from foot to foot, hands in pockets, as he tried to prepare me for likely disappointment. 'Don't be surprised if it's rejected straight away.'

I wasn't expecting a sudden acceptance of my theories. I was fully aware that there were other examples in healthcare of patients being misguided by conflicting information. In a *British Medical Journal* article entitled 'The Shameful Past[97]', I had read about the nicotine studies of the 1950s. As early as the 1940s, cigarettes were recognised as the cause of lung cancer. This was a result of research carried out from many different angles, including animal studies, reviewing pathology, analysing chemicals in cigarettes, and investigating the distribution of disease.

Despite all the evidence, the cigarette manufacturers denied the link. In fact, the tobacco corporations continued to advertise their products, brainwashing the public into thinking that the filters and other alterations to encourage nicotine addiction would lower their risk. But none of this changed the fact that cigarettes kill. This is strikingly similar to what's happening in the sugar industry now – will the people never learn? Will doctors never learn? By 1960, few doctors had truly accepted the real risk of cigarettes.

The author of the BMJ paper, Robert Proctor, who is a History of Science Professor at Stanford University, thinks that cigarettes are the most destructive invention. I disagree with this. My opinion, like many nowadays, is that cigarettes are probably the third deadliest after sugar and alcohol. It was clearly going to be a long journey.

I wanted to get my revelation known, although I was fully aware that there might be a backlash from certain industries, which would undoubtedly seek to ridicule me, just as they had done to Yudkin, who told us that sugar was killing us. I figured that if I at least had the support of a leading British journal, I would be in a stronger position to argue my case. This was to be my mark in the sand. Hopefully, it would set in motion a wave of research aimed at seriously reducing diabetes, heart disease and dementia, rather than pussyfooting around with yet more genetic research, which was unlikely to lead to a rapid cure for these diseases, now reaching epidemic proportions. I was convinced that I had enough evidence to support my claim that thiamine destruction by bacteria in the gut was important in many disease processes, and, more importantly, that dementia was easily treatable with drugs that are readily available and not even heinously expensive.

I spent hours writing and rephrasing my article and asked close colleagues, friends and family to proofread the final draft. My medical journal of choice was *The Lancet*, as they will accept papers that have a plausible hypothesis, particularly a multifaceted hypothesis that may be difficult to prove. I felt that trying to push the idea into the scientific arena would be difficult, yet I didn't think it needed to be so if it could gain the interest of an academic with the right know-how and facilities.

Whilst actively seeking the right platform to do my own research and approaching scientists and gastroenterologists with my theory, I had been dismayed and disgusted to be fobbed off with excuses such as, 'Research into this is unlikely to get funding, as the drugs are too cheap,' or 'The hypothesis is too broad,' or even 'Thiamine couldn't possibly be implicated in all these conditions.'

The counterarguments to my hypothesis were endless: 'It's all too vague,' or 'Too lightweight,' or 'All over the place,' and finally, 'Disorganised.'

I was told that 'Any research grant reviewer would be confused and would reject this.'

Reading between the lines, I had to face facts that I was too old, wasn't a professor or was the wrong gender.

If I was unable to get a grant to undertake the research – and I certainly wasn't able to experiment on patients without a proper research set-up, as this is wholly unethical – then the only way forward was to publish my hypothesis and try to persuade someone with more credibility to undertake the research.

With resolute excitement, I duly wrote a covering letter and submitted my article to *The Lancet*. Dr Dixon, the great scientist . . .

The article began by summarising the hypothesis in the abstract.

Hypothesis:

The metabolic syndrome is primarily due to thiamine deficiency, as a consequence of thiamine degradation by intestinal bacteria.

Jo Dixon

I was pleased with my introduction. I thought it made the case clearly. Matthew helped me with the wording and the Einstein quote I included: 'If at first an idea is not absurd, then there is no hope for it', which amused us both. I continued by summarising the papers that I had found on bacterial overgrowth, supporting my argument by linking together the evidence. I was pleased when I found there was support for my hypothesis from mouse models – the fact that the metabolic syndrome could be triggered by intentionally giving mice small intestinal bacterial overgrowth. Diet alone did not improve the metabolic syndrome. This seemed to translate well to the human condition.

I then used the Lakhani study, which had demonstrated that thiamine deficiency could be cured with antibiotics, and the information I had gleaned from looking into the complications from jejunoileal bypass surgery, which demonstrated that thiamine deficiency is caused by gut stasis. There followed the paragraphs on the underlying biochemistry, including the fact that thiamine is essential for all living things, because without it respiration, the release of energy from food, is impaired, which I suggested could be omitted, but pointed out that a failure to understand this basic concept explained why we are still in the dark ages regarding the diagnosis and treatment of dementia and the metabolic syndrome.

One of the issues with the metabolic syndrome that I had failed to address was the associated inflammation, however, I found evidence that if the normal metabolic pathways fail, inflammatory cascades are invoked. Nitric oxide build up is known as a proinflammatory mediator. I explained that phytanic acid seemed to be key in these processes. Reading through everything again, it seemed ultra complicated, and yet so simple. A lack of certain enzyme functions results in an increase in unwanted chemicals and a deficiency in others.

I summarised the conditions that are associated with thiamine deficiency in humans and in animal models, and those conditions that had responded to thiamine treatment. I really wanted to get across the fact that beriberi differed widely in its presentation in each individual. In effect, it was the first syndrome to be discovered – a constellation of symptoms and signs, which are not necessarily present in each case.

I then wrote about my theories on diet, mentioning that reducing dietary carbohydrate changes gut bacterial flora. Similarly, eating a high-carbohydrate diet alters the gut bacteria, and this seems to affect the thiamine-dependent pathways. In non-alcoholic fatty liver disease, a high-carbohydrate diet is associated with increased inflammation, whilst a high-fat diet is associated with lower levels of inflammation.

I wrote about my theories regarding the protective effect of red wine, and how moderate wine drinkers have a lower risk of all cause mortality, and specifically neurodegenerative diseases such as Alzheimer's and Parkinson's disease, cardiovascular disease and certain cancers. The antimicrobial effect of red wine is well documented, and is partly due to plant phenols, especially resveratrol. Resveratrol, found in grape skin, is produced as part of the natural defence mechanism against bacterial or fungal infections. The popular diets recommend increased fruit and vegetable intake and reduced carbohydrate, or they promote periods of fasting; each diet reduces carbohydrate intake or increases the natural antimicrobial content of food, hence reducing bacterial load.

As no article on thiamine would be complete without a review of the discovery, I described the experiments that involved feeding red rice and white rice to chickens. I emphasised that initially beriberi was thought to be an infectious disease. It was interesting that despite elaborate research into the cause of these outbreaks of beriberi and searching for thiaminase in food and heavy metal ingestion, studies often did not test the stool for thiaminases. I then described how thiaminase is fundamental to my hypothesis, and referred to the study in Melanesia.

My concluding paragraph ended with what I hoped was an accurate summary of why each nation needed to take on board this change in concept. In line with standard practice, I then had to admit to any dodgy business deals or to any drug manufacturers who might have paid for glossy trips abroad.

After writing 'nothing to disclose', I would have liked to have added, 'except a personal interest due to my ill health and a potential lasting cure for my own condition', but I restrained myself from doing so before sending my article off.

The Lancet Peer Review Team

To: Jo Dixon

Your submission to The Lancet

3 March 2014 13:10

Manuscript reference number: THELANCET-D-14-01433

Title: The metabolic syndrome is primarily due to thiamine deficiency as a consequence of thiamine degradation by intestinal bacteria.

Dear Dr Dixon,

Many thanks for submitting your manuscript to The Lancet. We have considered your manuscript, but our decision is that it would be better placed elsewhere.

Unfortunately, we can accept only a very small proportion of the many papers we receive each week. We are sorry to be unhelpful on this occasion, though we would like you to think of us again in the future.

Yours sincerely,

Yvette Ring

Senior Executive Editor, The Lancet

As Nick had predicted, it was rejected before the end of the day. I would need to take another route in my quest to bring this into the public domain.

A Novel Approach

THE MORE I SEARCHED FOR DATA TO SUPPORT my belief that thiamine was destroyed or removed by gut bacteria, the more confirmation I found in articles and papers that featured mainly in specialised journals or in those written decades ago. The names on the articles showed how scientists seemed to be insular in their approach to research and were often unaware of evidence from the animal world or from other medical disciplines. I was right – the vogue for research into nutrition had lost its appeal. Once a vitamin preparation had been produced that could replace the specific deficiency there was no longer any requirement for research into this vitamin. The germ theory in relation to diseases – the fact that bacteria might cause them – was really outmoded. My reading wasn't restricted to one area or idea, it was 'all over the place', and as a result it was as though I was standing back, looking onto the research field and surveying what was overtly clear – thiamine deficiency *is* the cause of the metabolic syndrome.

Even if I could make people listen to me, change would be unlikely, as people are reluctant to alter old habits, even when they know how much harm can result. You only had to stand outside the hospital entrance or drive past the local city college to see the numbers of people puffing away on cigarettes to realise that people find it easier to ignore evidence – often until it is too late.

The only way to make a difference seems to be to find a way

to make money out of it. It sounded cynical, but maybe people would listen and pay attention. And pay money!

Matthew was immediately interested in this approach and, after discussing it with a friend and neighbour who happened to be in the legal profession, he arranged for us to meet a patent lawyer in Cambridge. There seemed no embargo on patenting an idea, even if the proof wasn't there. The lawyer sent us to another lawyer who would draft up the papers, and we returned home to rewrite our paper in a completely different style.

Instead of writing a scientific paper with a summary first (the abstract) then the background, methods, results, discussion, conclusion, followed finally by references, the patent application had the order in reverse, starting with the conclusion (the field of the invention). The references were included in full in the text. I thought this made it difficult to read. The application was set out in clear sections (0001, 0002, and so on). The patent started with the clear statement:

<u>A novel approach to the management of degenerative, neurodegenerative, functional and metabolic disease processes.</u>

[0001] This invention relates to the role of bacterial thiaminase in human intestinal flora on thiamine absorption in various disease states and the treatment for this.

We worked on the patent application each evening. It was good to finally be including Matthew in my research. He was much better at the process and also understood the business aspects, such as protecting the idea and to which country we should apply for intellectual property rights. Finally, with the help of a patent advisor, we sent it off and waited in trepidation for the major breakthrough.

We were informed that the idea was not original. It was all a costly disappointment, which, in retrospect, was not really a great surprise. I felt like I was going round and round in ever decreasing circles. My hypothesis was neither accepted nor original, so where did that leave it? In the murky, grey depths of the sea of human knowledge? I was bitterly disappointed over yet another failure. Apparently, it was not possible to patent an idea. You need a product or proof.

I looked to see if the products I had been taking had patents, and they did. The producers of Rifaximin had patents for its role in diabetes, neurodegenerative diseases, fibromyalgia and irritable bowel syndrome. The company had also established a patent for the use of the antibiotic in dementia treatment, so why wasn't anyone doing the research, or, even better, using it?

It seemed that the way to patent anything was to submit a patent application for each potential future use. These guys didn't seem to need any proof, only a product and an idea. The multimillion-pound companies may well be able to afford to do this, but we couldn't. We had to admit that we were out of our depth – we did not belong in the same league.

Matthew had obviously enjoyed the experience. He tried to reassure me that rejection often happened and that on the back of one idea another would follow, which would turn out to be successful. I was not so sure, but nevertheless I started to think about a product based on my ideas.

I wanted to be able to test thiaminase in stool, or, even better, in the intestines. There was a test for *Helicobacter pylori*, the bacteria that had been found to cause peptic ulcers. This test uses the unique ability of this organism to produce an enzyme called urease, which breaks down urea. It simply measures the change in acidity due to the breakdown products, which is then linked to a colour change in a pH indicator. It was set up in a plastic container rather like those used for contact lenses, only smaller. In the small container was a jelly known as agar, a plant-based substitute for gelatin, which is also used to make desserts set. In this case, it provided nutrition for the bacteria. Endoscopy nurses carried out these tests all the time. The result was often rapid, sometimes within 15 minutes, and so by the end of the endoscopy it would often be possible to tell the patient if they had an *H. pylori* infection. A prescription for a course of antibiotics could then be written. It was called a 'CLO' test – Campylobacter-like organism – named after the original term for the *H. pylori*. It had been invented and patented by Barry Marshall, the doctor who infected himself with this bacteria. The test was supposed to be left for 24 hours before declaring it was CLO negative (if there was no colour change) or CLO positive, indicating the presence of *H. pylori* in the sample of intestinal mucosa.

The problem with my hypothesis was that as yet there were no reliable tests for small intestinal bacterial overgrowth. The best test was the glucose hydrogen breath test, but the results were still unreliable. Instead of blindly testing for an increased level of bacteria in the small intestines, I wondered whether it would be possible to test for specific bacterial products, especially if these products were potentially harmful. After all, many bacteria were thought to be beneficial. I speculated that it would be possible to test for thiaminase in a similar way to urease, using the breakdown of thiamine instead of urea, and likewise linking it to a colour change. I was no chemist, but I did try to look into assays and methods. A strip test would be a fantastic way of doing things. It might even be able to incorporate *H. pylori* and other bacteria.

In addition, there was also an elastase test for stool, so perhaps the test could be adapted to look for thiaminase in stool, and I could compare the results to see if it was a reliable indicator of potential negative thiamine status in the population.

The more I thought about it the less ridiculous it seemed. The remit was to make a bedside test that could be used in GP surgeries, endoscopy units and hospital wards, etc. Tests for thiaminase existed, so I simply had to work out a way to link it to a colour or pH change. The initial tests had involved radioactivity, and that was definitely not something I wanted to carry out at home. More recently, thiaminase had been detected using a chemical reaction with a substitution for thiamine. The resultant chemical changed the wavelength emitted, and this could be detected using a piece of equipment called a spectrophotometer. This would be expensive – spectrophotometers cost thousands.

I fondly recalled working in the labs in Southampton, and later on in Cambridge. The close location of each lab, off a corridor near the ward area, meant that practising doctors could feasibly carry out research. Back then it would have been possible for me to learn how to use a spectrophotometer. I would have been able to arrange for samples to be sent from the endoscopy suite. In my hospital, the nearest spectrophotometer was on a completely different site.

These days, complex ethical forms had to be completed and large amounts of money were required. Although I could probably access the forms, the money was a different proposition; as far as I could see, all of it now went to genetic research. Without money or forms I had no access to the machines I needed. I thought about looking on eBay. Matthew's friend, Steve, bought everything on there, including drums and guitars, but not, as far as I knew, medical equipment. Would Matthew notice a spectrophotometer in the outbuilding? Once I had hidden his birthday present for a whole month in the ironing cupboard, where it had remained undetected.

I was reluctant to purchase a second-hand machine that may not work well and that I'd have to use without any laboratory support. There were reports that it was possible to use a mobile phone as a spectrophotometer to detect a change in light wavelength. It would require a specific software program, a dark room and some basic equipment, but it seemed feasible. I thought I would leave this as a backup plan.

I resorted to the papers again and reread one from 1952 by Professor Fujita, a Japanese biochemist.[98] He had experimented using thiaminase I from three different sources: shellfish, fish and bacteria. He measured the breakdown of thiamine using thiaminase activated by the addition of different organic bases. These are substances in chemical reactions, which predominantly contain hydrogen and carbon, and in aqueous solution release hydroxide ions containing electrons (OH^-). He found that the addition of certain bases that were aromatic amines – aromatic (ring-like structure, often scented) amine (attached to an amine NH2) – markedly accelerated the reaction. We now know that this is a substitution reaction and the aromatic amine acts as a nucleophile, donating electrons. The thiamine is cleaved in two and the thiazole is substituted by the aromatic amine.

I looked at the list and recognised that the most potent activators of bacterial thiaminase were quinoline, pyridine and aniline, in descending order. With more research, I found that quinoline is a yellow dye often used in the food industry. For example, it is used to dye smoked haddock. This meant that there would potentially be a change of wavelength affecting the visible spectrum – possibly an obvious colour change. I knew aniline was a dye used in the leather industry. I researched pyridine and discovered it had no distinguishing features other than an offensive stench. As it was colourless it was of no use to me. I glossed over this detail and thought I would start with a few basic ingredients and test the water (no pun intended!).

Matthew fixed a bench in an outbuilding. I collected an old barstool from the black barn and found two old A4 hardback lab books with plenty of paper left. I relabelled the red covers 'Day book' and 'Lab book'. I also put my name on the books, even though it was unlikely anyone else in the house would pick them up by mistake. The children were unlikely to suddenly develop an interest in science; in their minds, scientific experiments were dull. I now had a lab off the kitchen at home, instead of one off the wards in the hospital! I wrote up the methods used for the detection of thiaminase in biological samples. It was like following a recipe and there was a short list of ingredients that I would need to source: thiamine solution, phosphate buffer, and the dyes aniline or quinoline. I looked online for chemical sales and placed an order. I had used this chemical supply company before, when I worked in the lab, but I hadn't ordered any of the chemicals I needed back then. I received an immediate reply:

Good morning

Thank you for your purchase order.

As we have not been able to locate a Sigma-Aldrich Account Number, which matches the address details stated on your commerce order, we are unable to proceed and your order has been cancelled.

This was going to be more complicated than I thought. It looked like I needed a laboratory, as a residential address was clearly unacceptable (although I struggled to work out how I was going to make a detonator using thiamine solution and the dyes). Admittedly, the buffering solutions used for the phosphate buffer could be misused. There had been several recent incidences of acid attacks. Despite the frustration at being refused, I was actually pleased that there were stringent checks on people ordering. I now needed an alternative plan: hire a lab, ask a friend or make do *Blue Peter*-style. I opted for the latter.

I reviewed my list of ingredients and decided to see if I could source them elsewhere. I had a pot of thiamine tablets, although each tablet contained other ingredients and I wondered if this would be an issue. The thiamine was the mononitrate compound, as opposed to the thiamine hydrochloride more commonly used in scientific experiments. I used a pestle and mortar to grind the tablets and added water. The resulting solution was cloudy, hence some of the ingredients in the tablets were insoluble. According to my research, both thiamine hydrochloride and mononitrate compounds were soluble in water, hence I assumed it was the other chemicals in the tablets that were insoluble and therefore of no consequence.

I also need to source the dyes. I ventured to my local supermarket to buy yellow food colouring, rather naively hoping that it would be quinoline, which unfortunately it wasn't. However, it didn't take me long to find a company selling it – a supplier of professional cookery equipment and ingredients from southwest France. It amused me to think that the company must have assumed I was a professional chef. My order was delivered within three days. Aniline was also easy to source. I found a helpful leather restoring company in Scotland and ordered the yellow powder from them. I knew I had to be careful with it though, as its use has been linked to bladder cancers.

A buffering solution was more difficult. The phosphate buffer really was preferable, so I looked up the exact proportions of the two different sodium phosphate compounds I'd need to make it. I rationalised that as thiaminase is extremely stable at body pH, any solution intended for the human body should be neutral; I bought contact lens solution hoping that it would have a pH of 7. I also bought soda crystals and clear spirit vinegar in case I needed to adjust the acidity or alkalinity, and distilled water for the thiamine solution.

I now needed to find a source of thiaminase. Having moved next to the river, where there was the best carp fishing in Norfolk, I was briefly tempted to get out a rod and reel, but I resisted this, realising I had no expertise, or for that matter a permit. I felt certain that the best source of thiaminase would be poo. People collect all sorts of things, but there were definite issues with this. I wasn't sure how willing people would be. Or even if they were, would it be the right kind of thiaminase-containing poo? Would I collect anonymous poo, or name it? If they weren't anonymised samples, I would run into ethical issues immediately. How would I go about it?

I imagined saying, 'Hello, I'm Jo, can you let me have a sample of your poo? Just leave it on the side, no need to name it.'

My mother helpfully offered to collect poo from her friends. I'm really not sure how she proposed to do this. I imagined the conversation: 'Next time you do a number two, could you save it for my daughter? More tea, Mary?'

Then there was the transport. It wouldn't be wise to post the poo. Imagine if it leaked! Frozen poo was a possibility using dry ice, but this was still fraught with difficulty. I remembered how foolish I'd thought my old university friend Heather was for experimenting on flatus, and my change in standards left me bemused. I queried how she managed to transport the gas. I tentatively questioned whether my own faeces would still contain bacterial thiaminase, but I thought this was unlikely as I had taken multiple courses of antibiotics, and I was now feeling well without needing to take them. Then there was storage. I didn't particularly want to store the samples in our freezer. I briefly considered buying another one, but thought I should try to get the experiments working before making any major investments. Besides, in the lab the research freezers were all −80 degrees centigrade. They would not be considered eco-friendly, and the girls would no doubt have something to say about that. What was I thinking anyway? Experimenting on poo was a ridiculous idea.

Back down on earth, I ordered the fern called horsetail or Equisetum. All horsetail species produce thiaminase. The species I ordered online was *E. Hyemale*. As a child, I had seen these plants growing wild. They were like mini Christmas trees, except that they had jointed stems, which could be pulled apart. I remembered my mother telling me that these plants had been around when dinosaurs roamed the earth. It seemed she was right: some members of the family of Equisetum had been around 350 million years ago, forming forests, and are therefore now responsible for coal deposits.

Equisetum reproduced by spores, which is similar to the bacteria *Clostridium*, and this allows them to survive in harsh environments. There are many different *Clostridium* species. The most familiar is *Clostridium difficile*, which can cause diarrhoea in patients who have been recently hospitalised, are immunosuppressed or have recently taken antibiotics. Unless cleaning is conducted to an exceptionally high standard, the spores can survive on a hospital ward. Just as thiaminase proffers a survival advantage, so too does producing spores.

Equisetum (horsetail) is also known as 'scouring rush', as it has been used for polishing or scouring metal and pewter. A high silica content gives it this property. It also means that it is sold as a herbal medicine, because the silica supposedly improves general wellbeing. The idea of taking a compound that contains thiaminase seemed utter madness. At least there is a warning on most packets against taking it in pregnancy, or long-term.

I explained to Matthew about the email from the chemical company – Sigma-Aldrich – and he contacted them to explain that we were serious about research and that we had formed a company. After completing various forms explaining the details of the experiments we were intending to conduct and before I ordered any of the chemicals, I received another email:

New Account Application

Good Afternoon

I am pleased to inform you that your new account has now been authorised and is ready to use.

Our Ecommerce team has advised me that we have been unable to proceed with the order you placed online (prior to your account being opened).

Please be kind enough to place your order again.

And another:

> Thank you for registering with Sigma-Aldrich.com.
>
> Due to the nature of the products we sell, setting up your account for ordering can take several business days. You will be contacted by our local office about the status of your account.

And another:

> Thank you for placing your order online with Sigma-Aldrich.
>
> Since this is your first order, we will review your application for ordering access before processing the order.
>
> When ordering access has been approved, you will receive [a] notification and an order confirmation email containing your order number.

I decided I would keep Sigma-Aldrich as a backup and continue with my high-street experiments. I bought plastic artist's palettes, with deep wells, and labelled them accordingly. I planned to keep a note in my daybook along with photographic evidence of the experiments conducted. I also needed a new pestle and mortar to grind up the horsetail, rather than using the kitchen one. I didn't want to contaminate our food with thiaminase, or whatever else I decided to experiment on. I found a large one made of grey granite – ideal for my purpose – and used rinsed glass jars for the various stock solutions: thiamine, aniline and quinolone. I also located some leftover clear heparin syringes, which I washed out. These had measurements on the side so I could draw up the correct amount of solution. I spent some time 'guestimating' the mass and therefore the 'guess-proximate' concentration of my solutions.

The horsetail didn't thrive. Admittedly, it was still only March and it was cold, but I was too impatient to wait. I limited myself to 1cm pieces of the plants. The thiaminase was supposed to be found in the entire plant, including the stalk, although I thought I had read somewhere that it is present in a higher amount in spring growth.

Finally, I was ready to begin. I used a syringeful of the thiamine solution in all the experimental wells and aniline in six experimental and six control wells, repeating the pattern with quinoline. Finally, I added my magic horsetail mixture and waited for the colour to disappear in the experimental wells. I took photographs to help me compare. The colour didn't obviously fade immediately, but it was difficult to be sure as the yellow dye was certainly less vivid. I made a hot drink while leaving the experiment to develop. Upon my return, I found that all the wells were, well, murky green.

I reworked my calculations. Perhaps the thiaminase was too weak. I used 2cm of plant and diluted the dye. The result was the same – khaki green. I tried a heated tray to speed up the reaction. Still no success. Admittedly, most scientists had included a centrifuge step, using gravity in a small machine to spin the samples of thiaminase, ensuring that the solid (green) matter would drop to the bottom of the eppendorf container (small plastic tube). I didn't have the tubes, or a centrifuge, although once again I looked up how feasible it would be to buy one. Most centrifuges were affordable, but the ones I needed were exceptionally pricey. Instead I opted for filtering the sample. The only filters I had were coffee ones. This didn't really work, as I lost the entire sample in a soggy wet filter along with the green, stringy remnants of the plant. How frustrating!

I considered the reasons why the experiment wasn't working (apart from the fact that I had none of the correct equipment or chemicals) and decided that I should check the pH of my chemicals. Thiaminase is inactivated at certain levels of acidity and alkalinity, and the optimum pH varies according to the source of the thiaminase. I briefly considered buying a universal indicator, but reconsidered when I remembered that red cabbage gives you an impressively accurate pH guide. (The pigment in red cabbage is called anthrocyanin and it turns red in acid, blue in neutral and yellow-green in alkaline solutions.) I ordered the red cabbage on the supermarket delivery that week – real scientists may have Sigma-Aldrich deliver their chemicals, I had Tesco!

I now felt confident this experiment would work. I chopped up the cabbage and boiled it in water. Once the water had turned a deep indigo colour, I then sieved out the remaining pieces and poured the solution into a jar. I now had a stock solution of red cabbage indicator to use in my experiments, and I found some very good images to establish the colour scale online. I poured vinegar into the wells and then the contact lens solution, adding soda crystals to adjust the pH. The pH in the contact lens solution needed adjusting. Perhaps this was why the experiment hadn't been working. I adjusted it to a physiological pH and retried, to no avail.

I had all but given up when Becky came to stay. I had updated her regularly on my progress, or not, in the laboratory. She was very keen to get involved. I had another plan, but first I had to explain the science behind the experiments to my enthusiastic lab assistant.

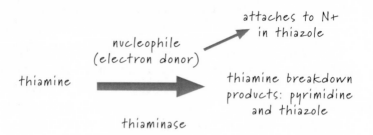

I started with a simple diagram then explained where the various chemicals fitted in:

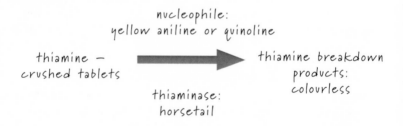

I found talking everything through with Becky helpful. I was able to tell her my plan for a bedside test, and that any sample in a GP surgery would not be centrifuged. I explained the methodology and we went shopping on the high street for more ingredients – I mean, chemicals.

Back in the lab (well, actually the kitchen – it was rather cold in the lab and the next step involved warming), I reflected on my earlier good fortunes with the water bath all those years ago, when I had inadvertently boiled my islet cells to discover a new function for the regenerating gene, and wondered whether this was where my luck would change. The plan was to dissolve agar and allow it to set with the thiamine and quinoline. These tester units would be ready for samples. What I hadn't explained was that the samples would now need to contain bacterial thiaminase. I wasn't sure how I would obtain these. For now, the plan was to set the agar. We 'guestimated' the amount of agar and water required and boiled it in a saucepan. We then added the thiamine and quinoline. Becky asked a pertinent question on the thermal stability of thiamine – it probably isn't too stable. That would have to be dealt with on another day; for now, we were trying to set the agar, hopefully with an obvious yellow tinge. The first step involved following the instructions on the back of the agar pot. How difficult could it be? Unfortunately, the yellow agar didn't set at all. After Becky left I retried with double the amount of agar and no additional ingredients – it set firm.

I wasn't sure of the next step and was beginning to run out of horsetail plant. The charade was becoming tiring. I needed to order the proper chemicals and laboratory equipment. I made a note of everything I required and an approximate cost. But it wasn't the money or the time that concerned me, it was rather my loss of faith and self-belief. Even if I did make a test for thiaminase in my outhouse, would anyone take me seriously? I placed my high-street chemicals in a plastic box and tidied my lab bench, reflecting that it was a useful space for a number of other purposes.

Whilst explaining the details of the experiment to Becky, I learnt another interesting fact. Nicotinic acid acts as a nucleophile for thiaminase, enabling it to break down thiamine into unusable products. Nicotinic acid is a product of the oxidation of nicotine, and I wondered if this happened in lit cigarettes. Perhaps smokers, harbouring thiaminase-producing bacteria in their guts, would then have activation of this thiaminase? Nicotinic acid is actually vitamin B3. I wasn't sure it was even found in cigarettes, but there are other organic chemicals that activate thiaminase that are contained in so-called 'cancer sticks', such as phenylalanine, tyrosine, pyridine and acetophenone. Do these make smokers more prone to thiamine deficiency? The chemicals would have to be swallowed. This would mean that for patients trying to quit smoking, presumably nicotine patches would be better for thiamine levels, but vaping would potentially be as bad as cigarettes. Interesting that vaping is now known to be harmful, as it causes chemical injury to the lungs . . .

Enterohepatic Circulation

HAVING DISCOVERED NUMEROUS PAPERS from decades ago, I continued to retreat into the depths of scientific literature. I just could not believe there were still so many unanswered questions. Perhaps we weren't asking the right ones, or, if we were, listening to the answers; maybe we just hadn't revisited the problem.

Reading about thiamine was taking me further and further into the archives. The relevant research had all taken place in the 1940s and 1950s. One article by Pecora showed how chronically thiamine-deficient rats had alterations in their electrocardiogram – the ECG, or electrical activity of the heart. There were abnormalities in the ST and T waves and rhythm disturbances.[99] How many times had I seen such abnormalities in patients? As they had no chest pains and their blood tests were normal, it was considered to be an irrelevant finding. The author of this article had also looked at organ function in thiamine-deficient rats and reported that they had abnormalities in the heart muscle, specifically the atria.[100]

It was interesting to read that low thiamine affects the atria. Cardiac problems associated with wet beriberi were well recognised, but this specific defect was not something I had read about before. Perhaps this was one of the reasons why patients develop atrial fibrillation. Often patients with this drank too much alcohol, others had been exercising hard; both alcohol and exercise reduce thiamine levels.

I also read that furosemide, a diuretic which is widely used in heart failure, lowers thiamine levels by increasing urinary excretion[101, 102]; adding another drug, spironolactone, increases thiamine levels.[103] Studies have since shown that patients fare worse on furosemide[104] and longer-term outcomes were better on spironolactone.[105] More intriguing was the fact that cognitive decline was ameliorated in mice administered spironolactone, but the benefit was only seen in female mice.[106] I wondered whether spironolactone would be as beneficial in patients with dementia as it had been for those with heart and liver failure. I felt certain that by changing furosemide to spironolactone, the underlying mechanism had to be an improvement in thiamine status. As seen in patients suffering from beriberi, only a proportion of the rats had problems. After all, the presentation of thiamine deficiency is very varied. One of the problems researching in this field is the lack of standard response to treatment, because of this variability.

I read about the other organs affected; the rats' testes were found to be atrophic.[100] Infertility again! I was pleased that my hypothesis was holding true. I also questioned why there was a female preponderance for dementia and why women were more prone to alcoholic liver disease. Female hormones seem to be protective before the menopause. I considered that it could be due to a change in colonic transit related to the female sex hormone, which may then result in an increase in gut stasis and bacterial overgrowth after the menopause. There was some evidence to suggest progesterone may have an impact on gut transit and an acceptance that sex hormones do play a part in gut motility, with no clear idea how.

The female hormones are related to steroids. I searched for articles on steroids and thiamine deficiency, hoping to find a study and an explanation. All I could locate was a line in another Pecora article[107] quoting two other scientists. Pigeons with thiamine deficiency were apparently protected by male and female sex hormones. But this was being looked into back in 1937. I really was scraping the barrel of the archives. Most men do not have a menopause and testosterone is produced throughout their life. Women lose the protection of the female hormones after the menopause, unless these are replaced with synthetic versions. It was not only the sex hormones, however – vitamin D also relieved the symptoms of thiamine deficiency.

When I reread the paper summarising the treatment of mice with spironolactone, I realised that it was an effect of this class of drugs – a group of medicines with a similar structure. Female mice with diabetes benefitted more from spironolactone than the male mice. The beneficial effect of spironolactone disappeared in female mice treated with oestrogens.[106] Spironolactone not only works as a diuretic, it is also an androgen receptor antagonist. It blocks testosterone, but has some oestrogen effects. It seemed that the spironolactone protected against thiamine deficiency, as well as potentially increasing thiamine levels. I knew there had to be a link. This was it.

For a long time, I had simply assumed that vitamin D deficiency occurring due to bacterial overgrowth was important in its own right. In a way, it was a useful marker of bacterial overgrowth. In the absence of direct tests for thiamine deficiency, it was also a reasonable surrogate marker of the condition. It would explain why studies administering vitamin D to patients did not universally improve the condition, as the vitamin D administered orally would presumably fail to be absorbed. It would also explain why prescribing an antibiotic improved patients' vitamin D levels and often their condition, too. I even wondered whether the 'immunological' properties of the class of antibiotics such as tetracycline were due to the effect on vitamin D absorption or, what was probably more likely, the combination of thiamine and vitamin D absorption. It seemed that it was now more complicated and that vitamin D actually protects against the effects of thiamine deficiency, as well as improving the natural antimicrobial defence in the gut. Hence, in small intestinal bacterial overgrowth, the malabsorption of both vitamin D and thiamine would have dramatic effects.

I was interested in the structure of the various sex hormones and any similarities. Estradiol and testosterone have an identical ring structure, with different side chains. Steroids, such as cortisol, also have the same basic ring structure as the sex hormones, as does spironolactone. In fact, spironolactone was synthesised to compete with the steroid hormone aldosterone, hence its steroid ring structure.

I tried to find out how these hormones might protect against thiamine deficiency. One article described how oestrogen induces certain biochemical pathways that enhance the mitochondrial function and sustain the Kreb's cycle.[108] The signalling pathways were extremely complex so I couldn't determine exactly how the thiamine-dependent pyruvate dehydrogenase enzyme was bypassed, but perhaps it was possible. Another article confirmed that low levels of testosterone were associated with an increased risk of Alzheimer's disease.[109] Oestrogen works by increasing the number of glucose transporters in the brain, so that more glucose is taken up. The brain primarily uses glucose as a fuel, and one way to get around not being able to use glucose fully is to take up lots of it.[110] Perhaps the hormones aren't protective, they simply upregulate other pathways to try to cope with a deficiency. The menopause changes the distribution of body fat, increasing central adiposity, which is one of the metabolic syndrome criteria. Interestingly, administering oestrogen prophylactically doesn't reduce the cardiovascular disease risk (perhaps thiamine is necessary as well). Similarly, administering testosterone to patients with Alzheimer's dementia can be detrimental and exacerbate their neuropsychiatric symptoms.

I started to question whether there really was a gender difference, as I had been led to believe. It seems that there is no major difference in the incidence of the metabolic syndrome between males and females.[111] Likewise, the dementia incidence is similar for men and women.[112] Perhaps it is just that women live longer and men die of other causes.

One of the things I had struggled to explain was the loss of the effect of the intravenous thiamine after only 48 hours. I knew that exercise used up thiamine, and I recalled rushing around after the first time I received an infusion of vitamins. Subsequently, though, any beneficial effect had worn off within 48 hours of each infusion, even if I had been sitting quietly doing jigsaws. I had read about a so-called enterohepatic circulation for vitamin D, and also remembered being taught about it in the pharmacology lectures at Southampton. Essentially, vitamin D and certain drugs were excreted into the bile and then reabsorbed into the circulation through the gut. This could have an effect on the levels. An article in 1975 reported on studies in humans using radioactive vitamin D. One hour after the injection, a third of the vitamin was secreted into the bowel and then 85% was reabsorbed.[113]

This point was brought home several years later when I attended an update course for general medicine run by some Cambridge physicians. One of the speakers had an interest in vitamin D metabolism and he related a clinical case: a patient on TPN (total parenteral nutrition) had been receiving vitamin D injections, but despite this she remained severely deficient in the vitamin. I instantly knew why. She obviously had bacterial overgrowth associated with stagnant guts. The gastroenterologist explained to the doctors present that this was due to the enterohepatic circulation. I looked around. No one seemed to be taking in the importance of this fact. The other doctors were busy gazing out of the window or were discretely texting or checking the news or weather. They were more interested in the snow forecast and whether it would disrupt their journey home. Some seemed to be taking notes, but on closer inspection I saw that they were actually only making intricate doodles of spiders' webs or annotating their programme.

I wanted to stand up and make them understand. *This is fundamentally important.* If you learn nothing else today, then you need to remember this. I didn't stand up, but I did get a jolt of electricity as I felt the brain waves connect. This would explain it! I suddenly realised the significance. The lecturer must have wondered why I was looking smug as I beamed up at him . . . at least I wasn't inadvertently winking any more!

There must be an enterohepatic circulation for thiamine too. Thiamine must be excreted in bile, and in normal physiological states it must be reabsorbed from the intestines into the portal vein and back to the liver. Thiamine is not stored, but surely it should remain in the system for more than 48 hours. In the presence of thiaminases or defective thiamine transporters, reabsorption will be impaired and hence the effects of intravenous thiamine would be short-lived. I wasn't sure if this had ever been documented; it certainly wasn't well known. I had circumvented this by taking benfotiamine each day. Not only is this better absorbed, but thiaminase does not destroy it – presumably its structure is not recognised by the enzyme.

The enterohepatic circulation was also important for preventing gallstones; hypersecretion of cholesterol in the bile also prevents stone formation. There seemed to be recognition that bowel transit time was prolonged in patients with gallstones and that excess carbohydrate or high sucrose in the diet increases faecal bile salt loss. I understood this to be due to an alteration in the small intestinal bacteria and a reduction in the reabsorption of bile salts. The final chink: gallbladder motility is impaired in these patients.

Sugar, bacteria, dysmotility – once more reiterated: this is thiamine deficiency in another guise.

Using this theory, I wondered if I could explain the wider benefits of other drugs, for example statins. Statins are extensively used to reduce cholesterol, which they do very effectively by blocking the enzyme 3-hydroxy-3-methylglutaryl-CoA reductase. For this reason, the scientific and class name is HMG-CoA reductase inhibitors. Bacteria require HMG-CoA reductase to produce cholesterol to maintain a cell membrane; hence statins are actually very effective antimicrobial agents. However, they also have a beneficial effect on patients suffering from respiratory tract infections, but the dose required to kill a bacteria in the chest is far higher than that present in the blood. It has been known for a while that statins have a beneficial effect in patients beyond just lowering their cholesterol. Perhaps this is due to it reducing the bacterial load in the small intestines and therefore increasing thiamine and vitamin D levels. By rectifying the thiamine and vitamin D status, the patient's immune function would also improve . . .

★

We were sitting in the garden drinking tea. Matthew's friend, Steve, was visiting.

'I quoted you the other day,' he started telling us, 'a mate just stopped taking his statins. That makes no sense to me. As far as I'm concerned, we should all be on aspirin and statins.' Steve had recently been started on statins to lower his cholesterol. 'As usual, middle-aged men talking about their bowels,' he continued.

I wasn't sure where this was leading, but I watched Matthew's face for a response. He carried on slurping tea from a mug.

'Regular as clockwork!' Steve proudly announced. 'Ever since I started statins, my bowels are as regular as clockwork.'

I was about to reiterate my theory – these discussions were no longer private or confined to the breakfast table – but then Steve offered up more evidence. 'They used to be all over the place ...'

'More tea?' Matthew changed the subject quickly before the conversation became too graphic. We never did find out what he'd been 'quoting' us on. Perhaps he had accepted my gut bacteria theory and the importance of diet after all. In the meantime, I had picked up on his comment and was already nodding to myself; he probably had an element of bacterial overgrowth and the statins helped. He certainly had an unhealthy diet and was fond of sweets and chocolate. He used to joke that he only visited us to get his 'five-a-day' and one visit a month was enough to satisfy his requirement of such horribly healthy fare. I was interested in this new theory about statins but had to admit it was n=1 again.

I wished I had read more before speaking to Richard about my proposal for a research study using benfotiamine and rifaximin to treat fatty liver. As with many of the papers I had come across recently, I couldn't quite remember what had made me click on the abstract. Scrolling through one, however, I noticed a line that made me gasp. In 1959, this researcher had administered thiamine injections to thiamine-deficient rats and discovered that the amount of fat in the liver is mainly controlled by thiamine.[114] This was definitely the cause of fatty liver – the metabolic syndrome I had been interested in all along. Thiamine deficiency causes fatty liver and thiamine injections can treat it. It explains why not everyone who is obese has fatty liver. Those patients with thiamine deficiency are prone to fatty liver. Cholesterol was also higher in the thiamine-deficient rats. Cholesterol is measured as a marker of the metabolic syndrome. It was proposed that the thiamine-cholesterol pathways should be investigated.

There was evidence to support my hypothesis wherever I looked. I was really excited when I read an article by Tanaka.[115] In animal models, thiamine treatment prevented obesity and the metabolic syndrome, with incredible results; rats genetically prone to develop metabolic syndrome have marked fatty liver, but simple treatment with thiamine in their drinking water made the fat disappear. In the journal, there were before and after colour photos of the liver with large globules of fat, which vanished with thiamine treatment. I wish I had shown this to Richard. The seesaw diagram for metabolic syndrome in the liver (non-alcoholic fatty liver disease, or syndrome X) was beginning to take shape.

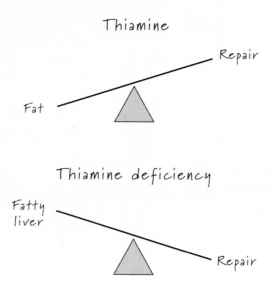

So Keys was partially right. Cholesterol is associated with human disease; only it is not dietary cholesterol that is important, but the level of cholesterol in the blood. Reducing the amount of cholesterol in food doesn't reduce the cholesterol in the blood. However, eating more fruit and vegetables and less sugar will reduce cholesterol, because cholesterol in the blood is controlled by thiamine. The cholesterol-lowering drugs, such as statins, do work, but not simply by blocking cholesterol synthesis. I presume they also work by reducing gut microbes, therefore enabling thiamine absorption. Yudkin was also right; sugar increases human disease. He had shown that thiamine deficiency was an issue, but he had underestimated the importance of an imbalance of sugar and thiamine in human disease. Perhaps, like most people, he had assumed that thiamine deficiency was avoidable by supplementation.

I reflected on my earlier conundrum that not all heavy drinkers develop cirrhosis and wondered whether there was a similar mechanism; maybe it was the heavy drinkers with thiamine deficiency who were the ones that developed advanced liver disease. Matthew had been to an update meeting in London. As usual, there was little new information, however, he did report one interesting fact. The panel had been discussing the increase in the prevalence of liver disease.

'There was an inflection point in 1994,' he said. 'Coincidentally, this was about the time you wanted to become a liver specialist.'

He was right. It was shortly after that I had applied for gastroenterology training in Cambridge. I wondered why there was an increase in liver disease at that specific time.

Thiamine malabsorption as a result of the destruction or utilisation of thiamine by intestinal bacteria is the missing link. Bacterial overgrowth is exacerbated by sugar in the diet. The significance of vitamin D cannot be ignored. This vitamin is produced in the skin in response to sunlight. People living closer to the equator, therefore, have higher vitamin D levels. Plants also produce vitamin D when exposed to ultraviolet light, therefore plants grown closer to the equator have more of this vitamin. Living in Southern Italy, Keys would have had high vitamin D levels as a direct result of sunshine, and indirectly from his diet. Sex hormones are another matter. They seem beneficial but their exact role remains unclear. Perhaps both thiamine and sex hormones are required for the brain to function properly.

Thiamine alleviates the metabolic syndrome, which is due to thiamine deficiency in the presence of excess calories, as opposed to beriberi, which is due to thiamine deficiency in the absence of calorie excess.

Significantly, Alcopops were first launched in 1993. These ready-mixed drinks that tasted like pop and got you drunk were an immediate hit and the young people who consumed them were known as the 'alcopops generation'. But this popular beverage left its mark. In the decade after its launch, the hospital admission rate for severe alcoholic liver disease in the under 30s more than doubled. Sugar and alcohol – it's certainly a potent combination

Malrotation Case

I RETURNED TO WORKING FULL-TIME on the unit, doing the evening shifts, which often turned up interesting cases. During one, the emergency department referred a 22-year-old man to us. He was studying at the local university and was experiencing abdominal pain. The surgeons had already examined his abdomen and decided that there was no surgical cause for his pain. The patient had a soft abdomen and normal bloods. He had a history of irritable bowel syndrome and clearly this was a case of 'functional' bowel, or possibly gastritis. He admitted to drinking four pints of beer relatively swiftly the previous night, and the pain had started shortly afterwards.

I asked the patient questions and listened carefully to his answers. He explained that for as long as he could remember he had intermittently suffered from abdominal pains. He was clearly in severe distress and was alternating between writhing in pain and sitting on the hospital bed hunched over with his knees bent to his chest. This is an instinctive posture for someone in pain, but it's odd behaviour for a patient with either irritable bowel or gastritis. He had no scars on his abdomen and he didn't seem to be the sort of person who would put on an act purely to get a shot of morphine – a condition called Munchausen syndrome. I believed him. This was not simply a case of severe irritable bowel syndrome.

I requested a lactate test and discovered it was raised, indicating that somewhere in his body there was tissue metabolising anaerobically, which meant it was starved of oxygen or that its blood supply was compromised, as happens with twisted guts.

I had personally experienced a number of similar episodes and found that leaning forwards made the pain much more intense, as though a hot poker was being driven right through me. In fact, during these times my insides were twisting slowly and painfully. I had even been admitted to my own unit with pain, but as my blood tests were normal, I had been discharged with a diagnosis of gastritis, and probably stress. Fortunately, since the corrective surgery, I had suffered no further episodes.

Prior to the operation, I had learnt that the most comfortable position to lie in was on my back, although this was counterintuitive, as all I wanted to do was curl up in a ball, like the young man in front of me. Gradually, by lying on my back, the knife-like pain would resolve, although it would often still take an hour, becoming a dull, bruise-like ache rather than the intense, nauseating sensation. As I had an understanding of what happened in malrotation, whenever I had these pains, I was able to imagine my guts gradually untwisting and the blood supply slowly returning to the engorged muscles and vessels.

I arranged a CT scan for the patient, explaining to the rather glib radiology registrar that this man may have ischaemic gut, due to a lack of blood supply. Abdominal pains and raised lactate – it seemed a reasonable surmise.

'Have the surgeons seen him?' he asked.

'Yes, they assessed the patient in the emergency department,' I replied, knowing what was coming next.

'Do they think a CT scan is indicated?'

I found this infuriating. The surgeon who had seen the patient was a trainee who had qualified less than three years ago, compared to my 20 years of experience. The radiologist reluctantly agreed to do the scan, which showed that the patient had congenitally malrotated guts. He had an identical diagnosis to me, only it had been picked up two decades earlier. By drinking four pints of beer, presenting at the time when he was in pain, making a fuss rather than braving it out, and meeting me in the department, he had a diagnosis. All the holes had lined up in the Swiss cheese model of bon chance! What are the odds of this happening? How many other patients avoid the precipitating factors, just like Pavlov's dogs? They fail to visit the hospital acutely, and, like me on multiple occasions, find ways around the symptoms; by not eating in my case (males tend to present earlier with malrotation than females) or, like the patient with Addison's disease who took to eating handfuls of salt, they treat themselves. These patients are dismissed as being hypochondriacs when they do present. Functional! It's clearly an eating disorder! I was lucky to have worked with Fraser. My life would have been very different without the serendipitous intravenous thiamine.

The radiologist reported that there was no volvulus on the scan, although there was still swelling in the bowel wall showing that there had been ischaemia. I was fairly confident that once the patient had lain flat on the CT platform his twisted small bowel would have unravelled as the tension was removed. He returned to the ward smiling. Being a patient makes you a better doctor. Being a generalist enabled me to think laterally, across specialities.

I referred the young man to the surgeon as an outpatient and his malrotation was fixed before he had a chance to develop complications. In my own case, the path to surgery had been fraught with delays.

I recall another late shift on the unit. The nurses were struggling with a lady who was wandering over to other patients and fiddling with their belongings. In particular, she was taking their bottles and glasses of water from their bedside tables. The patients were upset by her behaviour, as she seemed to do it in an aggressive manner. The nurses asked if I could prescribe her something. I went over to talk to her. 'Are you thirsty?' I enquired as a starter.

The patient nodded.

'I'll get her a glass of water,' the nurse said. 'Would she like ice?'

The patient nodded again.

The glass of ice-cold water was brought to her table and I hoped to be able to alleviate some of her distress and find out whether there was a reversible element to her restlessness: infection, dehydration or simply confusion because she didn't recognise her surroundings. I could empathise with her and hoped I could help.

An increasing number of patients were seen on the unit with confusion or delirium. Sometimes, they were known to have underlying dementia, but as their condition had deteriorated the systems in place to care for them had failed. We would look for factors that might lead to a decline in cognitive function, such as polypharmacy – a cocktail of too many drugs interacting and causing unwelcome side effects; often the doses of drugs used in the elderly or infirm are too large, directly causing the deterioration. Other causes would be a fall, leading to a serious but unrecognised head injury – a slow leak of blood between the skull and the lining of the brain known as a subdural haematoma. Then there were the endocrine causes. It was particularly important to exclude hypothyroidism – an underactive thyroid gland. We would also want to exclude infection. A chest infection is usually obvious, but it was surprisingly difficult to diagnose a urinary tract infection, as a clean catch was hard – there was often stuff in the urine that could just be a contaminant. The current practice was to only treat a definite infection, which made perfect sense, but sometimes you just couldn't be sure. I would rather over treat than under treat infection, and it was surprising how often the patient's condition improved when this was done. Commonly, the results of the urine test would be returned with the comment 'likely contaminant', and any infection would be disputed. Strange, then, that the patient's mental status improved after the course of supposedly unnecessary antibiotics.

The confused patient I was now kneeling before, having placed the glass of water on her tray table, picked up the glass as if to drink it before throwing the ice-cold contents all over me. The other patients in the ward gasped in horror. I laughed. There was no other response. This lady had advanced dementia and as verbal communication was difficult for her, she responded with non-verbal communication. She was agitated and frustrated that the nurses were cajoling her into sitting in one place. She was clearly restless and probably disorientated by the strange surroundings. It was clear she didn't want to see me, and anyway, I surmised that I was unlikely to be able to help her. I doubted severe disease would be significantly reversible. Nerve cell regrowth is extremely slow, and likely to be retarded further in the elderly. Even now I am questioning my response. Should I have tried intravenous vitamins? Would it have worked?

The problem with dementia or brain failure is that there is no replacement therapy, such as dialysis. Transplantation is potentially an option for kidney and liver failure, but nothing can be offered for a failing brain. There needs to be a way to identify the disease at an early stage, when the condition is still largely reversible and therefore amenable to treatment.

It is possible that thiamine replacement may have alleviated some of the lady's agitation. But purely on a practical level, would I have been able to put a cannula in to give the infusion? Would it have been assault? I wouldn't have been able to get her consent for the treatment. Could I have treated her in her best interest when the treatment had no agreed proof of efficacy, even though I knew the evidence exists?

Abnormal Glucose Metabolism

WE DECIDED TO MOVE OUT OF THE HOUSE in the country. The children were growing up and preferred living in town. Their lives demanded better Wi-Fi and mobile phone reception and they resented the lack of convenient buses. It had also been difficult moving between the two properties. It was too easy to lose items, something I was fearful of doing, although now I had an excuse – moving! I was busy packing up belongings and memories, putting precious photos, cards and pictures in storage, unable to part with that part of the children's lives, whilst sorting through other boxes. The problem with space is that it gets filled. The house was cluttered. I thought back to Nana's house, still so clear in my mind, and wondered what memories my children would have of this one.

The country cottage had been a great family home. We had invested time and effort into the house and the surrounding land. There was space to spread out and a maze of rooms. We had added another staircase from the drawing room to the master bedroom, with a walk-through room joining it to the rest of the house. Children's parties were therefore great fun, especially playing sardines. There were so many places to hide and with two staircases it was an interesting place to discover.

Our last summer at the house, which we planned to rent out, was fantastic, with lots of the children's friends coming to stay, using the swimming pool and playing ball games in the garden. They had gathered around barbecues on the patio. Professionals had taken down the acre of greenhouse, which was modular and had been erected and then dismantled like an enormous Meccano set. It was split in half to be used as two separate greenhouses – it was too large for most businesses, hence it was going to two different sites. The old black barn had been cleared out and cleaned up. Using leftovers from the building works, the family had all helped to build a bar in the corner, where we hosted parties.

At the front of the property there was now a cottage garden, with peonies, roses, honeysuckle, delphiniums and lupins. The old pond had dried up when the greenhouse disappeared, as the water on the roof no longer drained away along the irrigation pipes. Instead, the saplings had taken root, especially a type of willow found locally – *Salix alba* (white willow). The undersides of the leaves shone silvery in the sunlight. The hollow had a coppice of silver birch and another coppice of larch. We had our own Dingley Dell.

Sadly, we no longer had chickens – one by one the fox had taken them. The orchard had matured and even the young Spartan apple tree produced abundant red, shiny apples. There were plums and greengages, quince and mulberries – if you could beat the birds to them.

The split-level courtyard had several doors leading out from the back of the house onto a sunken patio, with a massive soak away, which prevented any flooding. There were curved, stone steps from the kitchen, a feature point that reminded me again of Nana's house. We would often sit here. Lavender hedges lined the paths; there were climbing roses and wisteria on an arbor. As I packed up, I recalled the whole family sitting out there until late one night watching a meteor shower; I missed seeing most of the stars, turning too slowly, but had enjoyed relaxing in the company of my loved ones. I smiled to myself about the good times, remembering the hubbub and chaos and the constant chatter and activity of the years when the children were growing up. All the same, it was time to move on. I felt certain, however, that we would be back.

I gathered up the books from the bookcase – many unread, a few read but forgotten and the occasional one that had been read and reread. One book in this latter category was Yudkin's *Pure, White and Deadly*. Fraser had always believed my theory and had become obsessed with the hidden sugar content in many foods, such as the so-called healthy cereals and low-fat yoghurts, and the fact that low-fat food is not only tasteless, it doesn't lead to satiety, meaning that people tend to eat more of it. I remembered how much I had agreed with Yudkin, but I was now aware that he hadn't understood the whole picture. He hadn't been able to fully describe *how* sugar is killing us; he just knew it was. He hadn't explained the mechanism, only the various symptoms and diseases associated with excess dietary sugar – of which there are many. I suspected that a large number of these are inextricably linked to my thiamine deficiency hypothesis.

As I flicked through the pages of Yudkin's book, I read about acne and sugar, and wondered if this condition, too, could be in part due to thiamine status. After all, the disfiguring skin complaint often becomes a problem in adolescence when rapid growth spurts use up thiamine stores. Sugar cravings and consumption often increase at this age, too: cans of drink, sweet snacks or chocolate. It is curious that antibiotics should work for such conditions.

The book also had a section on sugar excess and indigestion. Fraser had commented on a marked improvement in his dyspeptic symptoms since embarking on the low-sugar diet. I found that I had stuck tabs on one page highlighting a sentence. Yudkin had shown that increasing sugar intake for just two weeks caused excess acidity in the stomach, not dissimilar to the levels seen in patients with peptic ulcers.

Yudkin's book had been written before Marshall had identified *Helicobacter pylori*. I recalled the number of patients I had gastroscoped in the endoscopy unit who had complained bitterly of indigestion, even though their stomach lining looked essentially normal, or, at the most, slightly pink. There was a vogue for starting these patients on proton pump inhibitors, a drug that almost completely blocks acid production in the stomach, rather than advising them to eat less sugar and ignore advice to follow a low-fat diet. I could now see that the practice of pharmacologically reducing stomach acid in a susceptible population would increase the risk of bacterial overgrowth. I had commented in my hypothesis that proton pump inhibitors, used widely in the Western world, increase the risk of small intestinal bacterial overgrowth, and had also mentioned that other treatments that reduce intestinal motility may also exacerbate overgrowth, such as opiates, anticholinergic and psychotropic medication used in mental illnesses.

I had highlighted another sentence in Yudkin's book. Some of his patients told him that they felt so much better on a low-carbohydrate diet that they were determined to stick with it. This was just what Fraser had said after giving up sugar. I had to agree with this sentiment.

After clearing the bookshelf, I packed up the contents of the filing cabinet in my study. I would no longer need the papers I had filed in the thiamine research section; they were mostly available online and storage was limited. I found one rumpled paper, which in the past I had obviously poured over many times. I remembered reading it and being thrilled at discovering that there was someone out there on the same wavelength as me.

Gibson was a New York-based neurologist. He had pointed out the similarities between the aberrant pathways in Alzheimer's disease and in diabetes.[116] He reported that in Alzheimer's there is always a decreased breakdown of glucose, as patients' brains aren't able to metabolise it. This deteriorated as the disease progressed, and was therefore an extremely good way of judging its severity.[116]

Gibson was unable to explain why there was such low glucose metabolism. I thought it was abundantly clear.

Thiamine deficiency! I wanted to shout out.

He redeemed himself by then giving a thorough review of the research into thiamine deficiency in Alzheimer's disease, and by the end of his paper you were left in no doubt as to the connection. In Alzheimer's disease, the brain develops plaques made of amyloid protein and 'tangles' made of tau protein. This tau protein is phosphorylated and then accumulates. An excess of plaques and tangles is seen in Alzheimer's and other degenerative conditions of the brain. In animal models, a lack of thiamine leads to the development of plaques and phosphorylation of tau. It also causes memory problems. Mice with Alzheimer's disease have been given thiamine in the form of benfotiamine, and this has reduced the plaques and improved their memory.

Researchers had used a new radioactive scanning technique (Fluoro-Deoxy-Glucose positron – a sub-nuclear particle produced by radioactive material – also known as a proton – emission tomography – FDG-PET) to investigate radiolabelled glucose uptake in the brain. I had underlined one sentence in the paper. I knew exactly what this was. Glucose metabolism is never normal. The brain primarily uses glucose as an energy substrate. Thiamine is crucial for glucose metabolism. As thiamine levels fall, dementia gets worse. Plaques are associated with thiamine deficiency. Benfotiamine reduces plaques. The messages couldn't be clearer. Put simply:

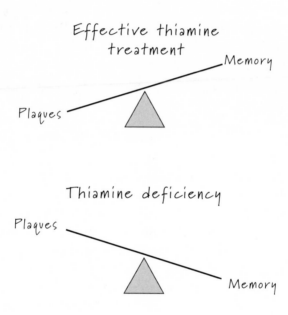

Previously, it had been thought that cirrhosis of the liver was due to excess collagen. Then my colleagues in the lab in Southampton, back when I was a medical student doing research and managing to boil my cells, suggested that it was due to insufficient protease breaking down the collagen. It seemed there was a similar mechanism in dementia – excess plaques, but the excess plaques aren't the underlying cause, they are the product due to insufficient metabolism or the perverted metabolism of the toxic by-products of sugar – due to thiamine deficiency.

I looked through the paper to see if Gibson had made the gut connection and the association with excess sugar and fructose or carbohydrates, but his was a well-written paper that had not drifted off topic, unlike my hypothesis, which I had been told was 'all over the place.' There was no explanation for the fact that oral thiamine supplements were not effective in Alzheimer's dementia.

I searched the internet for any further recent research using benfotiamine in Alzheimer's disease. There was still only Gibson's review article and the research into transgenic mice that he had quoted in his paper. Unfortunately, I knew from personal experience that simply treating patients with benfotiamine was unlikely to be successful. I felt sure that the average patient also needed to minimise alcohol intake, avoid certain other medications and control the amount of sugar and carbohydrates in their diet to reduce their bacterial overload. I then searched for benfotiamine, rifaximin and Alzheimer's disease. The response was abundantly clear:

We're sorry, but there were no items found for your search.

I threw Gibson's paper into the recycling pile and put Yudkin's book in the box. But he wasn't forgotten. He had been absolutely right about his discoveries, but these had been disputed and the sugar industry and other researchers had suppressed his revelations. What a different world it might be now if his work had been credited appropriately and he had been believed. When I first read his book, I recall being rather dismissive of his approach. He had seemed angry, needing to rant; now I understood why he felt this way.

At the bottom of a brown cardboard box was a black notebook. I looked inside and could see frantic scribbles and some illegible workings. The words I could make out looked like:

Metabolic syndrome, syndrome X, diabetes.

Other words occurred frequently:

Thiamine, thiamine def. deficiency.

There were flow diagrams, including terms such as:

Inactivating factors, sugar, bacterial overgrowth, thiamine destroyed by bacteria in the gut.

In the back of the notebook, there were my diary entries:

'Am just starting to go over and over things in my mind...'

Folded and tucked away in the slip of the back cover was a letter:

LIVING WILL

4th May 2012

To whom it may concern

For some time I have been suffering with a number of symptoms, which seem to have eluded medical science to date. Whilst I remain hopeful that my condition is treatable and the symptoms fully reversible, in the event of irreversible neurological, particularly brain or memory, impairment, I do not wish to be resuscitated <u>or</u> receive any active treatment that may prolong my life.

I am of sound mind when I write this and frightened that I may become dependent physically. I do not wish to be a burden, and would not like to survive in this state.

Jo Dixon (4/5/12)

Pre-Dementia Screening

OUR NEIGHBOURS IN TOWN INVITED us to a dinner party.

'I'm not surprised they haven't found a cure for Alzheimer's, they're looking in the wrong place!' I said, perhaps a little overconfidently, as the main course was served.

It was a bold statement, but one I felt I could argue and back up with science. The woman sitting next to me narrowed her eyes, raised her eyebrows and turned her head away from me; it was clear she wasn't remotely interested in my view. As far as she knew, I was a housewife and mother.

Attempting to restart the conversation, I asked, 'So what do you do?'

'I'm a professor of neuroscience,' she replied, with an air that invited no further comment on the matter.

The rest of the evening was a blur of superficial conversation and banter. I was cross with myself and felt disappointed for no rational reason. It was becoming clear that if I was going to get anyone to listen to my hypothesis, a fresh approach was required. Talking to strangers at dinner parties was unlikely to achieve anything.

★

There were some challenges to living in one place full-time. We had doubled the amount of stuff we kept at the town house, which had four staircases between five floors, including the cellar. All the gear migrated to the ground floor, unless I carried it upstairs or stored it in the basement, which resembled the black barn, only on a much smaller scale. The front door led out to the street and the boys were very obedient about removing their shoes as they entered. There was a small entrance hall, which opened into the only reception room. The hall was just about big enough to let you open the doors, but it meant the house operated a one-in-one-out policy. This was not the case for the shoes in the front room, which seemed to accumulate at an alarming rate, presenting an obstacle course.

Emily had her piano in the front room and the boys would often store bicycles, footballs and cricket gear there. There was a dining table to one side, which was usually covered in folders and schoolbooks. A shelf unit was heavily laden with piano and other music books, and well-thumbed piano music adorned the top of the piano and piled up on the table. There was constant activity in and out of this room, especially when the children brought home school friends.

The mess and general clatter and noise were not a problem, but the stench could be quite overpowering. Boys' trainers take on a personality of their own. A combination of sweaty feet and muddy pitch has a distinct aroma. Perhaps my sense of smell was returning.

I hadn't lost interest in resolving the riddle of Alzheimer's disease, but I began thinking of practical ways to screen patients, in order to identify the illness early and test patients objectively. I was fairly sure I could treat the disease, but recognised that treatment would be much more effective if started before it took hold. Early recognition was still out of reach.

Autonomic nerves lack the protective sheath, myelin – they are 'un-myelinated' and therefore more susceptible to thiamine deficiency. Autonomic dysfunction and the olfactory sensation – the sense of smell – are the first to be lost. (I never completely regained an acute sense of smell, despite it regularly being put to the test.) As we age, autonomic function does deteriorate, but unfortunately, testing for dysfunction is difficult. Electrocardiographs – line diagrams showing the electrical activity of the heart – may show an alteration in the normal variation in the heart rate, so-called sinus arrhythmia. As we breathe in and out, the heart rate increases and decreases as the parasympathetic nervous system responds to changes in thoracic pressure. This phenomenon is more pronounced in the young and is generally lost as we age. I recalled learning about it in medical school, but I wasn't sure if I had ever been told that it was abnormal to lose it. I accepted that it was part of the normal ageing process. I looked online to see if there was any information and found a study from 1976.[117] These investigators had looked for respiratory sinus arrhythmia in males aged between 21 and 65 years. There was a definite decrease with age, but about a quarter of the patients fell well below the best-fit line, or average for their age. It would have been interesting to know if these patients had suffered with any syndromes or cognitive impairment later in life, or even what their thiamine status was at the time of the study.

Another way of measuring autonomic dysfunction is using a sweat test. This is already used to screen for cystic fibrosis, the most common inherited condition, by detecting increased chloride concentration in the sweat. The test for autonomic dysfunction is called a thermoregulatory sweat test, and it involves lying in a sauna-like room and being covered in a moisture-sensitive powder that changes colour, from yellow to purple, as you sweat. Despite being a test linked to an obvious colour change, I wasn't sure how easy this would be to perform in a clinical setting – or how popular it would be.

I imagined seeing a patient in a dementia-screening clinic. 'Good morning,' I pictured myself saying. 'I'd like you to strip off, cover yourself in this powder and take a sauna ...'

The test also seems to be more complicated than simply measuring for a reduction in sweat, as sweating can increase if the nerve damage is extensive. Today, there are several other methods of testing available, but the simplest seems to be the 'sympathetic skin response', which detects changes in skin potential, rather than sweat, and has been studied widely by psychiatrists and the police, as it's also known as a 'lie detector'. Certain stimuli alter the skin potential, such as hyperventilation, emotion or electrical stimulation. It is assumed the skin potential is due, in part, to the response of the sweat glands and, therefore, acts as a surrogate marker for sweating and neuropathy. Abnormalities in autonomic function are seen in patients with Alzheimer's disease, particularly the loss of sinus arrhythmia.[118] Some of these patients also have abnormal sympathetic skin response in addition to loss of sinus arrhythmia – 5% in one study – but both abnormalities are found more commonly in other forms of more aggressive dementia, such as Lewy Body dementia.[119] Lewy Body dementia is associated with Parkinson's disease and the formation of Lewy Bodies – clumps of the protein alpha-synuclein. These differ from amyloid plaques and tau tangles. There was no evidence to suggest that the build up of alpha-synuclein or the degradation of this protein was related to thiamine deficiency or treatment.

Although I had lost my sense of smell and the ability to sweat, the earliest symptoms I experienced were gastrointestinal. It made more sense to screen patients complaining of unexplained, functional, syndromic symptoms, before definitive neurological dysfunction occurs. There may be some use for a 'lie detector' or even old-fashioned smelling bottles, or perhaps scratch and sniff cards. I would still have liked to set up an assay, but the high-street chemicals in my make-do lab did not yield any useful results.

I cast my mind back to all the strange events and unexplained illnesses. It wasn't just my illness. Why should the chicks in Norfolk have the same condition, particularly one where the symptoms seemed to match those of thiamine deficiency? The greenhouse had previously been used to grow green peppers with hydroponics. Sulphur is used to prevent mould and pests. Had they been poisoned by anti-thiamine factors such as sulphur?

The ducklings in Haarlem had also been affected by an illness, which was most likely thiamine deficiency. I realised that I hadn't considered it from this angle before. Initially, I was convinced that I'd suffered chemical poisoning; at the time I had spent hours thinking about whether the mushroom compost used to fertilise the garden had contained neurotoxins, or whether chemicals from the hydroponic systems in the old greenhouse had leeched into the soil. I thought about the polystyrene insulation that the chickens had pecked at until Matthew covered it up, but even that was supposedly inert and unlikely to have caused their disease. Once I knew that I had developed bacterial overgrowth, the problems with the chicks and ducklings no longer seemed relevant.

When I looked back, I realised that the only thing that was common to both Holland and Norfolk was my family, and I was the only one to have any problems consistent with thiamine deficiency. It was more than possible that the plumbing in the old house in Holland had been antiquated and leaky. Then afterwards, the sewage drains in our Norfolk home hadn't been working properly. In Holland, I had taken almost no antibiotics and until I stopped taking antibiotics back in England I had been well. Linking all of this together, I realised I had to be the carrier of the disease. I must have been passing the thiamine-destroying enzymes – thiaminase – in my stool and this must have affected the ducklings in Holland and the chicks in Norfolk. Could this really have happened – or was it simply too farfetched?

Dysphagia Lusoria

DISAPPOINTINGLY, I WAS INCREASINGLY developing problems with swallowing, which started with a ripping pain across my back, as if an artery was being severed. I reassured myself, in my usual way, that this was impossible. I was a fit, slim woman with normal blood pressure. I couldn't have arterial dissection.

I was used to avoiding bread and rice, but now even bananas were sticking behind my breastbone. Each time I ate anything I had a horrible sensation of a large lump in my chest and then the pain in my back started.

It was clear to me that the abnormal artery was impinging on my gullet. It was unfortunate, as the condition rarely causes significant dysphagia. However, I could tell I was developing dysphagia lusoria due to the compression of my gullet from my congenital abnormality. How unfortunate that both congenital abnormalities had caused me significant bother. I wondered whether I had deteriorated since losing such a considerable amount of weight, like the poor lady described by Bayford with the first case of dysphagia lusoria, who tragically starved to death. This seemed unlikely, though, as I had since regained the 10 kilograms. Then I remembered the endoscopy and the large probe pushed into my oesophagus, when they had used the ultrasound to look at my pancreas. The endoscopists had told me at the time that they had seen my aberrant artery. I developed intermittent back pains after this. These arteries are known to be weak; the procedure may have stretched the artery and caused it to tear.

I started losing weight again. I was on a liquid diet, taking regular high calorie drinks. Each time I had a busy shift at work I lost another kilo. I was becoming desperately thin and my colleagues thought I had anorexia nervosa. I had to admit that I was struggling to cope. I knew that the only way to correct it was to have more surgery. I hated the thought of this, but knew that I wasn't going to get better without an operation. I couldn't believe that I had to go through more surgery.

Reluctantly, I cleared my desk and inbox at work. I left a small pile of confidential papers in the corner of the office that I wasn't allowed to remove from the hospital. However, I had a sixth sense I wouldn't be returning. Surgery this time was a much bigger deal, with a much higher risk.

My last mission in the hospital was to see one of my clinic patients. As no more clinics were scheduled, I telephoned the patient at home to ask her to attend the unit. I was sure the nurses would understand, even though this wasn't strictly an emergency. The patient had been troubled by 'IBS' for a decade or more, but my specialist nurse felt that I might take a fresh approach and had specifically requested an appointment. On listening to the patient, I could see there was something that didn't fit for IBS – the symptoms were not consistent. The pains had become significantly worse, such that she was finding it difficult to eat.

It was possible that she had malrotation. I couldn't actually be sure, but I recognised that there was something wrong. It was almost as though her bowels were becoming obstructed. I didn't want the patient to be disappointed. I knew all about being let down – it had happened to me too often in the past.

I had to get the investigation done that day, because otherwise I wouldn't be able to easily hand over the case to a colleague. I wasn't practising medicine how I had been trained, but I had no choice if I was to get an answer before I left. I requested an urgent CT scan and waited in my office all afternoon for the results. I looked at the time on my phone. 4.30 pm and still no word. I had promised the patient I would be able to tell her the results that day. By 5 pm, I still hadn't heard and didn't want to risk the day staff in radiology leaving without giving me the result. Finally, I called radiology.

'The consultant is reporting it now,' the registrar replied.

At last the report was issued:

Thickening of the wall of the ascending colon. Need to exclude cancer. Further examination advised.

I hadn't expected this. This poor lady in her 30s had bowel cancer. Life was full of unpleasant surprises. At least it had been picked up at an early stage and surgery would cure her. If she'd waited another few months it might have been too late.

An hour later, I walked out of the hospital to prepare for the next chapter in my life: more surgery. I would not be able to complete the research to prove my theory and doubted anyone would believe me without more proof. Matthew believed me and so did Fraser. I had not succeeded in getting a grant. Perhaps the grant administrators were right, I was too old and past it. I had to face facts: trying to convince the world to change was a mammoth task.

Final Battle

WE INFORMED THE CHILDREN'S SCHOOLS about my operation and arranged for my mother to look after them whilst I was in hospital. The children gave me some presents and cards. I opened a piece of white paper, which had been folded in half to make a card.

Get WELL SOON!

To Mum,

Are you better yet - no?

Edward had made it for me. Inside he had written:

P.S. dont show this to enyone else or they will laghf at me.

There was a card of a chubby balloon man that Anna had made for me – my admission coincided with the screening of the cartoon film, *Big Hero 6*. It was inscribed:

HELLO I AM YOUR PERSONAL HEALTHCARE COMPANION.

Anna had written the words carefully, in contrast to the messy writing in Edward's card. He had probably rushed so he could go and play football with his friends. Anna had used pencil first so she wouldn't make a mistake. She had drawn

a superhero, in the form of an inflatable robot, to act as my
healthcare companion. She had then written over the pencil
in black ballpoint. Inside she had written:

I DREW A SUPERHERO BECAUSE HE'LL HELP YOU
RECOVER ☺

PS EVERYTHING IS A-OK AT HOME SO DON'T YOU FRET
ABOUT ANYTHING, JUST GET WELL!

PPS EXCEPT THAT LEONARD NIMOY DIED ON FRIDAY AND
NOW THERE IS A SPOCK-SHAPED HOLE IN MY HEART.

I was due to have surgery the following morning. Matthew
was aware of my living will. On the ward, I had signed all the
papers and seen all the relevant people. We had rewritten
our wills – I had been too weak to get out of the car so the
solicitor explained it to me from the back seat. Physically I was
frail. I had lost a lot of weight. There had been delays. I'd left
instructions with my mother that if anything happened to me
I wanted my book to be published.

That evening, Matthew said goodbye and left me in the
surgical ward. I doubted I would sleep. The lady next to me
behind the curtains had a large family visiting her. There was
loud conversation, partly in English and partly in a foreign
language, which I took to be an Indian dialect. They were
encouraging her to eat. The sister finally asked them to leave
and when they'd gone the patient started pacing around
in front of my bed. I recognised her apprehension. I didn't
know why she was there. I guessed she might have a heart
valve disease, such as aortic stenosis, a relatively common

problem causing narrowing of the aortic valve. I imagined that she had experienced angina-type chest pains because of restriction of the blood supply to the heart vessels. The origin of these vessels is beyond the aortic valve, and consequently impaired by the poor flow through the valve. Perhaps she had become breathless. She didn't look well. We exchanged well-meaning glances, wordlessly wishing each other good luck. She nodded her head sideways and put her hands together in a prayer fashion. I smiled uncertainly and nodded. We both understood that we were both scared. Scared of the pain? Not really, that was manageable and would resolve. Scared of permanent physical disability? Nervous, but as long as I had my mental faculties, I thought I would cope. Scared of dying? Yes. I really wanted to live. This time I wanted to fight.

★

'Can you look after Edward tomorrow after choir?' Matthew asked. He was struggling to fight back the tears as he spoke on the telephone to a close friend of mine, and a fellow chorister parent. Since the operation, he hadn't left my bedside. She could hear the guttural sounds of my breathing. I was kept in a coma, connected to the ventilator with tubes and drains everywhere. Matthew was used to seeing patients on the Intensive Care Unit, and recognised that the bleeding from drain sites and use of inotropes (drugs that tighten the blood vessels) to try and keep my blood pressure up was a bad sign. If the bleeding didn't stop I would need to return to theatre. There had been complications, too many complications. I probably wouldn't survive another operation.

Matthew spoke to my mother. He didn't often call to talk to her directly, but he wanted to prepare her, to alert her to the fact I may not pull through this time. He also wanted her reassurance that she would stay with the children and help them through if the worst happened.

Minutes seemed like hours and hours seemed like days. A decision would be made in the next hour if the bleeding didn't slow down. After a massive blood loss, my clotting function was deranged. I was also septic and acidotic (due to a build up of lactic acid, my blood pH was abnormally low); the more blood I lost the more acidotic I became, as my body wasn't being adequately perfused. The doctors were losing the battle.

Matthew stayed by my side until the early hours. Finally, the drain fluid eased; it was lighter in colour, which meant the bleeding had been stemmed.

★

I woke in pain, but I was relieved to be alive and to be able to move all my limbs, albeit with weakness on one side. Matthew wasn't there, but I was told that my guardian angel had stayed with me most of the night. Drains and tubes were exiting from every surface and limb. I assessed my state; it looked bad – bilateral arterial lines, bilateral central lines, feeding tubes, five drains, including one in the pericardium, which was draining the lining of the heart. This was far worse than I had expected. I was given a brief update on my results, which also weren't great, but at least I was alive. I requested more pain relief and questioned the antibiotics. I had insight – I'm sure I was easier to look after when I was sedated. I looked across the room and my fellow patient had survived the operation too.

I survived. There were multiple complications. I spent several days in the intensive care unit before transferring to the ward for what transpired to be a long period of recovery before eventual discharge. It was slow progress, but I made it out of there, unlike my fellow patient. She had to return to theatre. Her chances of surviving redo surgery were remote.

Life's Ups and Downs

LIFE HAS ITS UPS AND DOWNS, but the journeys now seemed smoother, the roads less bumpy, with fewer sharp turns and more vibrant colours. Even in winter, the pale yellow, milky sun has a certain beauty: a fragility and yet a promise of the future. The trees are outlined by a yellow halo long before the leaves are visible; a hint that full, vigorous growth is about to happen.

My experiences had made me realise what was important: family and health. And career? I wasn't able to return to work after the operation, which left me with a disability. I no longer have a direct blood supply to my right arm, which is wasted and much weaker. I often have pain and am limited in what I can do. One by one, each of my colleagues has also left my department in the hospital. Fraser went to work abroad, Nick to another hospital nearby. My two female consultant colleagues also moved on. They all had their reasons, but the truth was that the job had been too onerous and we hadn't received support from the management. There had been vacancies for years. It was going to be very difficult to replace five consultants. And me? The job had almost killed me. You had to be fit to do this kind of work. You had to be ultra-fit – 110% fit. I was far from well enough. I hated to admit defeat, but this had beaten me.

★

I hadn't been in this particular village church since Nana's funeral 34 years ago. That had been a sombre, sobering affair, and also very strange. As a 15 year old, I was unaware of the Quaker way, which was Nana's religion, and the culture of people being invited to speak their mind. We were sitting near the front of the church and behind us I was aware that the place was full – there weren't enough seats. There was a short service and then strangers started standing up and saying things – the first thing that popped into their minds, such as fragments of memories of Nana. I did not remain composed and thought these people were butting into a tragic, close family event. It seemed random – nonsense – but if I'd listened I may have learnt more about Nana, from friends, locals and people who really knew and admired her.

Nana would say things out of the blue, just like this. I remember asking her questions when my sister Becky and I were on one of her trails through fields and along hedgerows beside crops. I had been fascinated by the light, lime-green feathery barrels dangling on the hop plants, and by the pungent scent.

'Do you believe in life after death?' she enquired in a matter-of-fact tone, as though she were asking if we believed television was bad for children. Given our ages at the time, this might have been more appropriate. I hesitated, turning my face away from the hops and squinting into the sunlight.

'I do!' she announced without waiting for our reply. She had a habit of doing this. It was often blamed on her having poor hearing, but in actual fact her hearing was remarkably astute. There was to be no discussion. The subject changed immediately.

'This is *Alliaria petiolata*,' she said, pointing to a plant with bright green, spade-shaped leaves and delicate white flowers. 'Also called Jack-by-the-hedge.'

There was no way I was going to remember the Latin name, but I made an effort with the common name; for many years I was convinced it was Martin-in-the-fields, rather than Jack-by-the-hedge. I might have remembered the other common names, hedge garlic or garlic mustard, after its garlic and mustard scent and taste.

'This is wild horseradish. It has characteristic long leaves, like dock, and a distinctive smell. You just dig up the roots,' she told us helpfully. Although at the time this seemed rather pointless, as we clearly hadn't brought a spade on our nature walk, it is something I still remember.

Now I was back in the church, on the opposite side and near the front, for the funeral of an aunt who had died suddenly. Again, the church was full. This time I listened, and I learnt a lot about this lovely lady, who had been so popular, just like my nana. Before entering the church, my father had driven us to Nana's old house. I was stunned when he parked the car and walked up to the front door. The house was different yet still so familiar. The 'café window' was there, but the honeysuckle had gone. Often when you revisit places from your childhood they seem to have mysteriously shrunk. Nana's house had grown – the owners had extended it; however, even the old part was recognisably hers. The front door had been moved to the side, and the two cottages had been merged into one big house, with the same red tiles on the walls.

Dad boldly knocked on the door. I was excited. It was like being a small girl again.

'Hallo! Sorry to bother you. My name is Tom Armstrong. I used to live here with my mum, Renie, Renie Armstrong.' Dad was standing on the doorstep slightly awkwardly in his funeral suit and his hands in his pockets. It was a bit embarrassing, as the lady had clearly just stepped out of the shower.

'Renie Armstrong? Yes, I know. Do come in.' She stepped aside to let us into the hallway. She proudly showed us what they had done to the property and told us how the orchard had been completely destroyed by a storm a few years after Nana's death. I remembered picking up all those sticks from the ancient apple trees. These had been replaced and the new ones were healthy and thriving. Even the Dingley Dell was still there.

I looked around the hallway in wonder, as Dad and the lady chatted away about people and places they knew. The door ahead was propped open and a child was sitting at a breakfast bar in the new kitchen. Beyond that, the old kitchen was still recognisable. No longer as bright, but tidy and homely – Nana would have approved. The cosy room where we had celebrated our Christmases was no longer dark crimson, but a fashionable light grey. We were standing in the new double story extension, on the spot where the curved stone steps by the old front door once would have been. In the new hallway, I looked up and noticed an open-plan stairway leading up to the attic space, with windows in the roof. As I gazed out of them, at the light grey sky, I thought how I'd done my best. Nana would be proud.

★

In the months after the operation, I filled my days in the centre of town, observing passers-by. One of my regular cafés overlooked the market place and its brightly coloured yellow and white, green and yellow and yellow and red stripy roofs. I also frequented the café overlooking St Andrew's Hall, as it reminded me of the children's school concerts. There was always plenty of colourful human traffic to observe going to and from the arts university.

Inside the café, there was an eclectic collection of photographs, including my favourite of a Cuban lady wearing a bright yellow floral dress. She was tanned, with wrinkled skin from sun exposure and was smoking a cigar and smiling contentedly, looking as though she had flouted all the rules and lived life to the full. I admired her seemingly carefree approach to life.

I ordered a coffee and sat in the corner of the café on the bench, flicking through a magazine on the table. There was an interview with someone famous and I started thinking about my confident statement at the dinner party.

'I'm not surprised they haven't found a cure for Alzheimer's. They're looking in the wrong place!'

I imagined how an interview with me might read.

Do you really know the cause of Alzheimer's?

Yes, I do, and so do the scientists. Many cases are effectively metabolic syndrome of the brain due to thiamine deficiency with excess carbohydrate – all the evidence points to this as the underlying cause.

Do you know the cause of thiamine deficiency?

Yes, I do – thiamine is either lost, or used up, or not absorbed. In many cases, it's a combination.

Could you treat Alzheimer's dementia?

For the majority of cases, I believe the treatment is readily available, so yes, I could. Intravenous or oral, fat-soluble thiamine preparations are comparatively cheap. Reducing losses is important, so avoiding long-term furosemide, which increases urinary loss of thiamine. Thiamine deficiency also seems to occur as a result of sluggish bowels. This lead to bacterial overgrowth, which prevents thiamine from being absorbed. In these cases, antibiotic treatment would help. Gut stasis happens in a number of conditions, but one important example is Parkinson's disease. Patients with other chronic conditions are also at a higher risk of bacterial overgrowth, such as those with chronic pancreatitis, chronic liver disease and chronic renal failure. Other measures include limiting the use of acid suppression, such as proton pump inhibitors, another risk factor for bacteria overgrowth.

What else would you recommend?

As with all conditions, prevention is better than cure and, therefore, identifying patients at risk of thiamine deficiency or screening patients for thiamine deficiency is essential. Patients at risk include all those with 'syndromes', such as irritable bowel syndrome, chronic fatigue syndrome, restless legs syndrome, patients with mental health problems, particularly anxiety or insomnia, and patients with fibromyalgia.

Thiamine is used up in pregnancy and also with excessive exercise. Or it may be used up because of the disease process, for example, cancer cells proliferating rapidly. Or perhaps the body uses more thiamine whilst trying to repair damaged parts due to an underlying disease. Alcohol also reduces thiamine absorption. Preventing thiamine deficiency in these situations is important.

How could you test this hypothesis?

It is apparently difficult to accurately measure and interpret thiamine levels. Investigation of small intestinal bacterial overgrowth is not reliable. It is possible to test for faecal thiaminase, the bacterial enzyme that breaks down thiamine. Hence, the hypothesis could be tested in established dementia and then in future it may be possible to predict at risk populations. Increased prevalence of faecal thiaminase in populations may increase the risk of diseases associated with thiamine deficiency, such as diabetes in the Melanesian people. For research purposes, measurement of thiaminase in small intestinal aspirates would be potentially useful. Measurement of thiamine in the urine is a good way of checking that thiamine is absorbed. Therefore, it might be possible to measure an increase in urinary thiamine in patients with conditions known to be associated with small intestinal bacterial overgrowth before and after oral antibiotic therapy. An improvement in the condition in association with increased thiamine would suggest intestinal bacterial destruction of thiamine is the cause of the thiamine deficiency.

My imaginary interviewer had heard enough by this stage, and I was working back through the vast number of papers I had read and the various sources I had studied. It is now thought that Parkinson published his essay to encourage investigation of the disease he had described.[4] I would like to inspire research into the relevance of thiamine status in disease. Is it possible that people reading this will identify with some of the symptoms? It seemed to me that the original cause of beriberi wasn't quite so straightforward, and perhaps bacterial overgrowth had a role to play back then. The reduction in thiamine intake due to the milling of rice was an oversimplification. Rice bran also has antimicrobial activity against a variety of bacterial strains.[120] By mechanically removing the husk, not only was the thiamine content of the rice reduced, the antimicrobial protection was removed.

My hypothesis: **excess carbohydrate – intestinal bacteria overgrowth – thiamine deficiency** had been eluding scientists. Clearly, this connection, this missing link, explains the metabolic syndrome and associated conditions. Others had discovered parts of the equation, but hadn't completed it. It was only when I suffered with a dementing process, associated with marked vitamin D deficiency, which improved with intravenous thiamine and antibiotics, that I knew I was right.

I ended my hypothesis with:

We need to refocus on the importance of thiamine.

I consider myself lucky. Although I have a physical disability, mentally I am well. For a long time I lived in fear of becoming incapacitated, of dying prematurely, or worse, of living but being unable to look after myself. Thankfully, I am still able to remember, to think clearly, to communicate coherently and to appreciate life.

Postscript

Jo Dixon

To: Mum

Mum

I think you're already taking benfotiamine. I have attached a recent paper about a small cohort of patients with early dementia showing cognitive improvement after taking benfotiamine.[121]

Lots of love

Jo xx

Mum

To: Jo Dixon

Thank you, Sweetheart, I'll take a look at it.

I'm not on benfotiamine at the moment. Where would I get it from?

Lots of love

Mum

xxxxxxx

Sent from my iPad

Jo Dixon

To: Dad

Dad, just doing my usual scout through the dementia papers and thinking about whether to pick up my book again. Dementia treatments have been in the news again recently. The only treatments that receive tabloid recognition are the expensive, toxic, new ones.

This is a paper showing modest benefit of benfotiamine (safe, around for years, inexpensive) in patients with mild to moderate Alzheimer's disease. There is good evidence for thiamine deficiency in AD. I am fairly convinced that we are all borderline thiamine deficient. Alcohol only makes it worse. I am sure prevention is better than cure!

I reckon it is worth taking 1-2 capsules a day long-term. I buy the 250mg capsules and take two a day, which fits with the dose used in this paper.

You never know – might help you remember the fox trot more easily! ☺

Lots of love

Jo xx

Dad

To: Jo Dixon

Thanks, Jo. Apart from short-term memory issues and deafness that is no worse than in others of my age, I don't feel I'm drifting that way. But it's a small price to pay for preventing a deterioration that has not had time to be reduced in the human gene pool at our current excessive age. So I'll give it a go. I take it there are no interactions? I'll look around for the best price.

Love Dad

References

(i)   GBD 2016 Dementia Collaborators. (2019) Global, regional, and national burden of Alzheimer's disease and other dementias, 1990-2016: a systemic analysis for the Global Burden of Disease Study 2016. Lancet Neurol. 18(1):88-106.

(ii) Brookmeyer R, Johnson E, Ziegler-Graham K and Arrighi HM. (2007) Forecasting the global burden of Alzheimer's disease. Alzheimers Dement. 3(3):186-91.

1.   Asherton N. (1979) David Bayford. His syndrome and sign of dysphagia lusoria. Ann. R. Coll. Surg. Eng. 61(1):63-7.

2.   Section of Therapeutics and Pharmacology. (1936) The treatment of Addison's disease with salt. Proc. R. Soc. Med. 29(9):1137-45.

3.   Dale H. (1949) Thomas Addison: Pioneer of Endocrinology. BMJ. 2(4623):347-52.

4.   Donaldson IML. (2015) James Parkinson's essay on the shaking palsy. J. R. Coll. Physicians Edinb. 45(1):84-6.

5.   Pett KD, Willett WC, Vartiainen E and Katz DL. (2017) The Seven Countries Study. Eur. Heart J. 38(42):3119-21.

6.   Bontii J. In Indÿs Archiatri De Medicina Indorv Lib. IV. 1642. (Latin text).

7.   Leff RD, Towles W, Aldo-Benson MA, Madura J and Biegel AA. (1983) A prospective analysis of the arthritis syndrome and immune function in jejunoileal bypass patients. J. Rheumatol. 10(4):612-8.

8.   Clegg DO, Zone JJ, Samuelson CO Jr and Ward JR. (1985) Circulating immune complexes containing secretory IgA in jejunoileal bypass disease. Ann. Rheum. Dis. 44(4):239-44.

9.   Gamble CN, Kimchi A, Depner TA and Christensen D. (1982) Immune complex glomerulonephritis and dermal vasculitis following intestinal bypass for morbid obesity. Am. J. Clin. Pathol. 77(3):347-52.

10. Justus PG, Fernandez A, Martin JL, King CE, Toskes PP and Mathias JR. (1983) Altered myoelectric activity in the experimental blind loop syndrome. J. Clin. Invest. 72(3):1064-71.

11. Glad BW, Hodges RE, Michas CA, Moussavian SN and Righi SP. (1978) Atrophic beriberi. A complication of jejunoileal bypass surgery for morbid obesity. Am. J. Med. 65(1):69-74.

12. Jewell WR, Hermreck AS and Hardin CA. (1975) Complications of jejunoileal bypass for morbid obesity. Arch. Surg. 110(8):1039-42.

13. Halverson JD. (1986) Micronutrient deficiencies after gastric bypass for morbid obesity. Am. Surg. 52(11):594-8.

14. Lakhani SV, Shah HN, Alexander K, Finelli FC, Kirkpatrick JR, and Koch TR. (2008) Small intestinal bacterial overgrowth and thiamine deficiency after Roux-en-Y gastric bypass surgery in obese patients. Nutr. Res. 28(5):293-8.

15. Dukowicz AC, Lacy BE and Levine GM. (2007) Small intestinal bacterial overgrowth: a comprehensive review. Gastroenterol. Hepatol. (N Y) 3(2):112-22.

16. Vandenbrouke JP. (2013) Adolphe Vorderman's 1897 study on beriberi: an example of scrupulous efforts to avoid bias. J. R. Soc. Med. 106(3):108-11.

REFERENCES

17. Arnold D. (2010) British India and the "Beriberi Problem", 1798-1942. Med. Hist. 54(3):295-314.

18. www.nobelprize.org/educational/medicine/vitamin_b1/eijkman.htlm. Downloaded 10/06/18.

19. www.nobelprize.org/nobel_prizes/medicine/laureates/2005/marshall-bio.htlm. Downloaded 10/6/18.

20. Coats D, Shelton-Dodge K, Ou K, Khun V, Seab S, Sok K, Prou C, Tortorelli S, Moyer TP, Cooper LE, Begley TP, Enders F, Fischer PR and Topazian M. (2012) Thiamine deficiency in Cambodian infants with and without beriberi. J. Pediatr. 161(5):843-7.

21. Sniekers M, Foulon V, Mannaerts GP, Van Maldergem L, Mandel H, Gelb BD, Casteels M and Van Velthoven PP. (2006) Thiamine pyrophosphate: an essential cofactor for the alpha-oxidation in mammals — implications for thiamine deficiencies? Cell. Mol. Life Sci. 63(13):1553-63.

22. Würtz P, Soininen P, Kangas AJ, Rönnemaa T, Lehtimäki T, Kähönen M, Viikari JS, Raitakari OT and Ala-Korpela M. (2013) Branched-chain and aromatic amino acids are predictors of insulin resistance in young adults. Diabetes Care. 36(3):648-55.

23. McCormack SE, Shaham O, McCarthy MA, Deik AA, Wang TJ, Gerszten RE, Clish CB, Mootha VK, Grinspoon SK and Fleischman A. (2013) Circulating branched-chain amino acid concentrations are associated with obesity and future insulin resistance in children and adolescents. Paediatr. Obes. 8(1):52-61.

24. Hamaguchi S, Furumoto T, Tsuchihashi-Makaya M, Goto K, Goto D, Yokota T, Kinugawa S, Yokoshiki H, Takeshita A, Tsutsui H; JCARE-CARD Investigators. (2011) Hyperuricemia predicts adverse outcomes in patients with heart failure. Int. J. Cardiol. 151(2):143-7.

25. Buse MG. (2006) Hexosamines, insulin resistance, and the complications of diabetes: current status. Am. J. Physiol. Endocrinol. Metab. 290(1):E1-E8.

26. Schalkwejk CG, Stehouwer CD and van Hinsbergh VW. (2004) Fructose-mediated non-enzymatic glycation: sweet coupling or bad modification. Diabetes Metab. Res. Rev. 20(5):369-82.

27. Ojetti V, Pitocco D, Scarpellini E, Zaccardi F, Scaldaferri F, Gigante G, Gasbarrini G, Ghirlanda G and Gasbarrini A. (2009) Small bowel bacterial overgrowth and type 1 diabetes. Eur. Rev. Med. Pharmacol. Sci. 13(6):419-23.

28. Cuoco L, Montalto M, Jorizzo RA, Santarelli L, Arancio F, Cammarota G and Gasbarrini G. (2002) Eradication of small intestinal bacterial overgrowth and oro-cecal transit in diabetics. Hepatogastroenterology. 49(48):1582-6.

29. Virally-Monod M, Tielmans D, Kevorkian JP, Bouhnik Y, Flourie B, Porokhov B, Ajzenberg C, Warnet A and Guillausseau PJ. (1998) Chronic diarrhoea and diabetes mellitus: prevalence of small intestinal bacterial overgrowth. Diabetes Metab. 24(6):530-6.

30. Sabaté JM, Jouët P, Harnois F, Mechler C, Msika S, Grossin M, and Coffin B. (2008) High prevalence of small intestinal bacterial overgrowth in patients with morbid obesity: a contributor to severe hepatic steatosis. Obes. Surg. 18(4):371-7.

31. Madrid AM, Poniachik J, Quera R and Defilippi C. (2011) Small intestinal clustered contractions and bacterial overgrowth: a frequent finding in obese patients. Dig. Dis. Sci. 56(1):155-60.

32. Mathurin P, Gonzalez F, Kerdraon O, Leteurtre E, Arnalsteen L, Hollebecque A, Louvet A, Dharancy S, Cocq P, Jany T, Boitard J, Deltenre P, Romon M and Pattou F. (2006) The evolution of severe steatosis after bariatric surgery is related to insulin resistance. Gastro. 130(6):1617-24.

33. Meyrat P, Safroneeva E and Schoepfer AM. (2012) Rifaximin treatment for the irritable bowel syndrome with a positive lactulose hydrogen breath test improves symptoms for at least 3 months. Aliment. Pharmacol. Ther. 36(11-12):1084-93.

34. Pyleris E, Giamarellos-Bourboulis EJ, Tzivras D, Koussoulas V, Barbatzas C and Pimentel M. (2012) The prevalence of overgrowth by aerobic bacteria in the small intestine by small bowel culture: relationship with irritable bowel syndrome. Dig. Dis. Sci. 57(5):1321-9.

35. Weinstock LB and Walters AS. (2011) Restless legs syndrome is associated with irritable bowel syndrome and small intestinal bacterial overgrowth. Sleep Med. 12(6):610-3.

36. Weinstock LB, Fern SE and Duntley SP. (2008) Restless legs syndrome in patients with irritable bowel syndrome: response to small intestinal bacterial overgrowth therapy. Dig. Dis. Sci. 53(5):1252-6.

37. Thornalley PJ, Babaei-Jadidi R, Al Ali H, Rabbani N, Antonysunil A, Larkin J, Ahmed A, Rayman G and Bodmer CW. (2007) High prevalence of low plasma thiamine concentration in diabetes linked to a marker of vascular disease. Diabetologia. 50(10):2164-70.

38. Babaei-Jadidi R, Karachalias N, Ahmed N, Battah S and Thornalley PJ. (2003) Prevention of incipient diabetic nephropathy by high-dose thiamine and benfotiamine. Diabetes. 52(8):2110-20.

39. Alaei Shahmiri F, Soares MJ, Zhao Y and Sherriff J. (2013) High-dose thiamine supplementation improves glucose tolerance in hyperglycemic individuals: a randomized, double-blind cross-over trial. Eur. J. Nutr. 52(7):1821-4.

40. Costantini A, Pala MI, Tundo S and Matteucci P. (2013) High-dose thiamine improves the symptoms of fibromyalgia. BMJ Case Rep. doi: 10.1136/bcr-2013-009019.

41. Mastrogiacoma F, Bettendorff L, Grisar T and Kish SJ. (1996) Brain thiamine, its phosphate esters, and its metabolizing enzymes in Alzheimer's disease. Ann. Neurol. 39(5):585-91.

42. Meador K, Loring D, Nichols M, Zamrini E, Rivner M, Posas H, Thompson E and Moore E. (1993) Preliminary findings of high-dose thiamine in dementia of Alzheimer's type. J Geriatr. Psychiatry Neurol. 6(4):222-9.

43. Nolan KA, Black RS, Sheu KF, Langberg J and Blass JP. (1991) A trial of thiamine in Alzheimer's disease. Arch. Neurol. 48(1):81-3.

44. Schernhammer E, Hansen J, Rugbjerg K, Wermuth L and Ritz B. (2011) Diabetes and the risk of developing Parkinson's disease in Denmark. Diabetes Care. 34(5):1102-8.

45. Lu'o'ng Kv and Nguyên LT. (2012) Thiamine and Parkinson's disease. J. Neurol. Sci. 316(1-2):1-8.

46. Lu'o'ng Kv and Nguyên LT. (2013) The beneficial role of thiamine in Parkinson disease. CNS Neurosci Ther. 19(7):461-8.

47. Costantini A, Pala MI, Compagnoni L, and Colangeli M. (2013) High-dose thiamine as initial treatment for Parkinson's disease. BMJ Case Reports. doi: 10.1136/bcr-2013-009289.

48. Pai JK, Mukamal KJ and Rimm EB. (2012) Long-term alcohol consumption in relation to all-cause and cardiovascular mortality among survivors of myocardial infarction: the Health Professionals Follow-up Study. Eur. Heart J. 33(13):1598-605.

49. Arntzen KA, Schirmer H, Wilsgaard T and Mathiesen EB. (2010) Moderate wine consumption is associated with better cognitive test results: a 7-year follow up of 5033 subjects in the Tromsø Study. Acta Neurol. Scand. Suppl. (190):23-9.

50. Luchsinger JA, Tang MX, Siddiqui M, Shea S and Mayeux R. (2004) Alcohol intake and risk of dementia. J. Am. Geriatr. Soc. 52(4):540-6.

REFERENCES

51. Fall PA, Fredrikson M, Axelson O and Granérus, AK. (1999) Nutritional and occupational factors influencing the risk of Parkinson's disease: a case-control study in southeastern Sweden. Mov. Disord. 14(1):28-37.

52. Boban N, Tonkic M, Budimir D, Modun D, Sutlovic D, Punda-Polic V and Boban M. (2010) Antimicrobial effects of wine: separating the role of polyphenols, pH, ethanol, and other wine components. J. Food Sci. 75(5):M322-6.

53. Paulo L, Ferreira S, Gallardo E, Queiroz JA and Domingues F. (2010) Antimicrobial activity and effects of resveratrol on human pathogenic bacteria. World Journal of Microbiology and Biotechnology. 26(8):1533-8.

54. Jung HJ, Hwang IA, Sung WS, Kang H, Kang BS, Seu YB and Lee DG. (2005) Fungicidal effect of resveratrol on human infectious fungi. Arch. Pharm. Res. 28(5):557-60.

55. Bujanda L, Garcia-Barcina M, Gutiérrez-de Juan V, Bidaurrazaga J, Fernández de Luco M, Gutiérrez-Stampa M, Larzabal M, Hijona E, Sarasqueta C, Echenique-Elizonda M and Arenas JI. (2006) Effect of resveratrol on alcohol-induced mortality and liver lesions in mice. BMC Gastroenterol. 6:35. doi: 10.1186/1471-230X-6-35.

56. Malaguarnera G, Pennisi M, Bertino G, Motta M, Borzi AM, Vicari E, Bella R, Drago F and Malaguarnera M. (2018) Resveratrol in patients with minimal hepatic encephalopathy. Nutrients. 10(3):E329. doi: 10.3390/nu10030329.

57. Babacanoglu C, Yildirim N, Sadi G, Pektas MB and Akar F. (2013) Resveratrol prevents high-fructose corn syrup-induced vascular insulin resistance and dysfunction in rats. Food Chem Toxicol. 60:160-7.

58. Shang J, Chen LL, Xiao FX, Sun H, Ding HC and Xiao H. (2008) Resveratrol improves non-alcoholic fatty liver disease by activating AMP-activated protein kinase. Acta Pharmacol. Sin. 29(6):698-706.

59. Liu M, Alimov AP, Wang H, Frank JA, Katz W, Xu M, Ke ZJ and Luo J. (2014) Thiamine deficiency induces anorexia by inhibiting hypothalamic AMPK. Neuroscience. 267:102-13.

60. Muegge BD, Kuczynski J, Knights D, Clemente JC, González A, Fontana L, Henrissat B, Knight R and Gordon JI. (2011) Diet drives convergence in gut microbiome functions across mammalian phylogeny and within humans. Science. 332(6032):970-4.

61. Smith MI, Yatsunenko T, Manary MJ, Trehan I, Mkakosya R, Cheng J, Kau AL, Rich SS, Concannon P, Mychaleckyj JC, Liu J, Houpt E, Li JV, Holmes E, Nicholson J, Knights D, Ursell LK, Knight R and Gordon JI. (2013) Gut microbiomes of Malawian twin pairs discordant for kwashiorkor. Science. 339(6119):548-54.

62. Gannon MC and Nuttall FQ. (2011) Effect of a high-protein diet on ghrelin, growth hormone, and insulin-like growth factor-I and binding proteins 1 and 3 in subjects with type 2 diabetes mellitus. Metabolism. 60(9):1300-11.

63. Nuttall FQ, Schweim K, Hoover H and Gannon MC. (2008) Effect of the LoBAG30 diet on blood glucose control in people with type 2 diabetes. Br. J. Nutr. 99(3):511-9.

64. Solga S, Alkhuraishe AR, Clark JM, Torbenson M, Greenwald A, Diehl AM and Magnuson T. (2004) Dietary composition and nonalcoholic fatty liver disease. Dig. Dis. Sci. 49(10):1578-83.

65. Yudkin J. (1951) The vitamin B1 sparing action of fat and protein. 4. The effect of carbohydrate in diets deficient in vitamin B1 upon the survival and vitamin B1 content of the rat. Biochem. J. 48(5):608-11.

66. Lim DC. (2013) Sugar, not fat, is the culprit. BMJ. 347:f6846. doi: 10.1136/bmj.f6846.

67. Jackson T. (2013) How science is going sour on sugar. BMJ. 346:f307. doi: 10.1136/bmj.f307.

68. Capewell S. (2014) Sugar sweetened drinks should carry obesity warnings. BMJ. 348:g3428. doi: 10.1136/bmj.g3428.

69. Gomm W, von Holt K, Thomé F, Broich K, Maier W, Fink A, Doblhammer G and Haenisch B. (2016) Association of proton pump inhibitors with risk of dementia: a pharmacoepidemiological claims data analysis. JAMA Neurol. 73(4):410-6.

70. Zhou B, Huang Y, Li H, Sun W and Liu L. (2016) Proton-pump inhibitors and risk of fractures: an update meta-analysis. Osteoporosis Int. 27(1):339-47.

71. Billioti de Gage S, Bégaud B, Bazin F, Verdoux H, Dartigues JF, Pérès K, Kurth T and Pariente A. (2012) Benzodiazepine use and risk of dementia: prospective population based study. BMJ. 345:e6231. doi: 10.1136/bmj.e6231.

72. Manzardo AM, Pendleton T, Poje A, Penick EC and Butler MG. (2015) Change in psychiatric symptomatology after benfotiamine treatment in males is related to lifetime alcoholism severity. Drug Alcohol Depend. 152:257-63.

73. Livingston G, Sommerlad A, Orgeta V, Costafreda SG, Huntley J, Ames D, Ballard C, Banerjee S, Burns A, Cohen-Mansfield J, Cooper C, Fox N, Gitlin LN, Howard R, Kales HC, Larson EB, Ritchie K, Rockwood K, Sampson EL, Samus Q, Schneider LS, Selbæk G, Teri L and Mukadam N. (2017) Dementia prevention, intervention and care. Lancet. 390(10113):2673-734.

74. D'Aldebert E, Biyeyeme Bi Mve MJ, Mergey M, Wendum D, Firrincieli D, Coilly A, Fouassier L, Corpechot C, Poupon R, Housset C, and Chignard N. (2009) Bile salts control the antimicrobial peptide cathelicidin through nuclear receptors in the human biliary epithelium. Gastroenterology. 136(4):1435-43.

75. Evans CA, Carlson WE and Green RG. (1942) The pathology of Chastek Paralysis in foxes, a counterpart of Wernicke's Hemorrhagic Polioencephalitis of man. Am. J. Pathol. 18(1):79-91.

76. Honeyfield DC, Hinterkopf JP, Fitzsimons JD, Tillitt DE, Zajicek JL and Brown SB. (2005) Development of thiamine deficiencies and early mortality syndrome in lake trout by feeding experimental and feral fish diets containing thiaminase. J. Aquatic Animal Health. 17(1):4-12.

77. Wistbacka S, Heinonen A and Bylund G. (2005) Thiaminase activity of gastrointestinal contents of salmon and herring from the Baltic Sea. J. Fish Biology. 60(4):1031-42.

78. Linklater KA, Dyson DA and Morgan KT. (1977) Faecal thiaminase in clinically normal sheep associated with outbreaks of polioencephalomalacia. Res. Vet. Sci. 22(3):308-12.

79. Edwin EE and Jackman R. (1982) Ruminant thiamine requirement in perspective. Vet Res. Commun. 5(3):237-50.

80. Evans WC. (1976) Bracken thiaminase-mediated neurotoxic syndromes. Botanical J. Linnean Soc. 73(1-3):113-31.

81. Studdert VP and Labuc RH. (1991) Thiamin deficiency in cats and dogs associated with feeding meat preserved with sulphur dioxide. Aust. Vet. J. 68(2):54-7.

82. Lutnicki K, Madej E, Riha T and Kurek L. (2014) Polioencephalomalacia in ruminants caused by excessive amount of sulphur – a review. Bull. Vet. Inst. Pulawy. 58:321-6.

83. Earl JW and McCleary BV. (1994) Mystery of the poisoned expedition. Nature. 368(6473):683-4.

84. Nishimune T, Watanabe Y, Okazaki H and Akai H. (2000) Thiamin is decomposed due to Anaphe spp. entomophagy in seasonal ataxia patients in Nigeria. J. Nutr. 130(6):1625-8.

85. Kuku A, Okonji RE and Akinrinola BD. (2012) Comparative study of thiaminase in headfoot and hepatopancreas of Limicolaria flammea (Müller, 1774). Int. J. Biochem. Res. & Rev. 2(1):31-49.

86. Lee CF. (1948) Technological studies of the starfish. Part IV – thiaminase in starfish. Commercial Fisheries Rev. 10(5):12-9.

87. Hamada K. (1956) Studies on the disposition for the carrier of Bacillus thiaminolyticus Matsukawa et Misawa. II. Oral administration of Bacillus thiaminolyticus Matsukawa et Misawa to various animals. J. Vitaminol. (Kyoto). 2(1):72-7.

88. Douthit HA and Airth RL. (1966) Thiaminase I of Bacillus thiaminolyticus. Arch. Biochem. Biophys. 113(2):331-7.

89. Duffy P, Morris H and Neilson G. (1981) Thiamin status of a Melanesian population. Am. J. Clin. Nutr. 34(8):1584-92.

90. Citron KM and Knox R. (1954) The uptake of thiamine by a strain of Staphylococcus aureus from the duodenum of a case of polyneuritis. J. Gen. Microbiol. 10(3):482-90.

91. Müller IB, Bergmann B, Groves MR, Couto I, Amaral L, Begley TP, Walter RD and Wrenger C. (2009) The vitamin B1 metabolism of Staphylococcus aureus is controlled at enzymatic and transcriptional levels. PLoS One. 4(11):e7656. doi: 10.1371/journal.pone.0007656.

92. Toms AV, Haas, AL, Park JH, Begley TP and Ealick SE. (2005) Structural characterization of the regulatory proteins TenA and TenI from Bacillus subtilis and identification of TenA as a thiaminase II. Biochem. 44(7):2319-29.

93. Kimura Y and Iwashima A. (1987) Occurrence of thiaminase II in Saccharomyces cerevisiae. Experientia. 43(8):888-90.

94. Kraft CE and Angert ER. (2017) Competition for vitamin B1 (thiamin) structures numerous ecological interactions. Q. Rev. Biol. 92(2):151-68.

95. Sannino DR, Kraft CE, Edwards KA and Angert ER. (2018) Thiaminase I provides a growth advantage by salvaging precursors from environmental thiamine and its analogs in Burkholderia thailandensis. Appl. Environ. Microbiol. 84(18). doi: 10.1128/AEM.01268-18.

96. Acton DS, Plat-Sinnige MJ, van Wamel W, de Groot N and van Belkum A. (2009) Intestinal carriage of Staphylococcus aureus: how does its frequency compare with that of nasal carriage and what is its clinical impact? Eur. J. Clin. Microbiol. Infect. Dis. 28(2):115-27.

97. Proctor RN. (2012) The history of the discovery of the cigarette-lung cancer link: evidentiary traditions, corporate denial, global toll. Tob. Control. 21(2):87-91.

98. Fujita A, Nose Y, Kozuka S, Tashiro T, Ueda K and Sakamoto S. (1952) Studies on thiaminase. I. Activation of thiamine breakdown by organic bases. J. Biol. Chem. 196(1):289-95.

99. Pecora LJ, Ashburn LL and Hundley JM. (1950) Influence of rice and purified diets upon cardiac behavior of thiamine deficient rats. Proc. Soc. Exp. Biol. Med. 74(4):721-5.

100. Pecora LJ and Highman B. (1953) Organ weights and histology of chronically thiamine-deficient rats and their pair-fed controls. J. Nutr. 51(2):219-30.

101. Yui Y, Itokawa Y and Kawai C. (1980) Furosemide-induced thiamine deficiency. Cardiovasc. Res. 14(9):537-40.

102. Seligmann H, Halkin H, Rauchfleisch S, Kaufmann N, Motro M, Vered Z and Ezra D. (1991) Thiamine deficiency in patients with congestive heart failure receiving long-term furosemide therapy: a pilot study. Am. J. Med. 91(2):151-5.

103. Rocha RM, Silva GV, de Albuquerque DC, Tura BR and Albanesi Filho FM. (2008) Influence of spironolactone therapy on thiamine blood levels in patients with heart failure. Arq. Bras. Cardiol. 90(5):324-8.

104. Hasselblad V, Gattis Stough W, Shah MR, Lokhnygina Y, O'Conner CM, Califf RM and Adams KF Jr. (2007) Relation between dose of loop diuretics and outcomes in a heart failure population: results of the ESCAPE trial. Eur. J. Heart Fail. 9(10):1064-9.

105. Pitt B, Zannad F, Remme WJ, Cody R, Castaigne A, Perez A, Palensky J and Wittes J. (1999) The effect of spironolactone on morbidity and mortality in patients with severe heart failure. Randomized Aldactone Evaluation Study Investigators. New Eng J Med. 341(10):709-17.

106. Sakata A, Mogi M, Iwanami J, Tsukuda K, Min LJ, Jing F, Ohshima K, Ito M and Horiuchi M. (2012) Improvement of cognitive impairment in female type 2 diabetes mellitus mice by spironolactone. J Renin Angiotensin Aldosterone Syst. 13(1):84-90.

107. Pecora LJ. (1952) Electrolyte changes in tissues of chronic thiamine deficient rats and influence of certain steroids. Am J. Physiol. 169(3):554-60.

108. Brinton RD. (2008) Estrogen regulation of glucose metabolism and mitochondrial function: therapeutic implications for prevention of Alzheimer's disease. Adv. Drug Deliv. Rev. 60(13-14):1504-11.

109. Lv W, Du N, Liu Y, Fan X, Wang Y, Jia X, Hou X and Wang B. (2016) Low testosterone level and risk of Alzheimer's disease in the elderly men: a systemic review and meta-analysis. Mol. Neurobiol. 53(4):2679-84.

110. Shi J and Simpkins JW. (1997) 17 beta-estradiol modulation of glucose transporter 1 expression in blood-brain barrier. Am. J. Physiol. 272(6):E1016-22.

111. Bentley-Lewis R, Koruda K and Seely EW. (2007) The metabolic syndrome in women. Nat. Clin. Pract. Endocrinol. Metab. 3(10):696-704.

112. Ruitenberg A, Ott A, van Swieten JC, Hofman A and Breteler MM. (2001) Incidence of dementia: does gender make a difference? Neurobiol. Aging. 22(4):575-80.

113. Arnaud SB, Goldsmith RS, Lambert PW and Go VL. (1975) 25-Hydroxyvitamin D3: evidence of an enterohepatic circulation in man. Proc. Soc. Exp. Biol. Med. 149(2):570-2.

114. Williams JN Jr, and Anderson CE. (1959) Effect of thiamine deficiency and thiamine injection on total liver lipids, phospholipid, plasmalogen and cholesterol in the rat. J. Nutr. 69(3):229-34.

115. Tanaka T, Kono T, Terasaki F, Yasui K, Soyama A, Otsuka K, Fujita S, Yamane K, Manabe M, Usui K and Kohda Y. (2010) Thiamine prevents obesity and obesity-associated metabolic disorders in OLETF rats. J. Nutr. Sci. Vitaminol (Tokyo). 56(6):335-46.

116. Gibson GE, Hirsch JA, Cirio RT, Jordan BD, Fonzetti P and Elder J. (2013) Abnormal thiamine-dependent processes in Alzheimer's Disease. Lessons from diabetes. Mol. Cell Neurosci. 55:17-25.

117. Hellman JB, and Stacy RW. (1976) Variation of respiratory sinus arrhythmia with age. J. Appl. Physiol. 41(5 Pt 1):734-8.

118. Wang SJ, Liao KK, Fuh JL, Lin KN, Wu ZA, Liu CY and Liu HC. (1994) Cardiovascular autonomic functions in Alzheimer's disease. Age Aging. 23(5):400-4.

119. Negami M, Maruta T, Takeda C, Adachi Y and Yoshikawa H. (2013) Sympathetic skin response and heart rate variability as diagnostic tools for the differential diagnosis of Lewy body dementia and Alzheimer's disease: a diagnostic test study. BMJ Open. 3(3):e001796. doi: 10.1136/bmjopen-2012-001796.

120. Kondo S, Teongtip R, Srichana D and Itharat A. (2011) Antimicrobial activity of rice bran extracts for diarrheal disease. J. Med. Assoc. Thai. 94 Suppl 7:S117-21.

121. Pan X, Chen Z, Fei G, Pan S, Bao W, Ren S, Guan Y and Zhong C. (2016) Long-term cognitive improvement after benfotiamine administration in patients with Alzheimer's disease. Neurosci. Bull. 32(6):591-6.

Bibliography

Bliss M. (2007) William Osler: A Life in Medicine. Oxford University Press.

Bures J, Cyrany J, Kohoutova D, Förstl M, Rejchrt S, Kvetina J, Vorisek V and Kopacova M. (2010) Small intestinal bacterial overgrowth syndrome. World J. Gastroenterol. 16(24):2978-2990.

Iorio N, Malik Z and Schey R. (2015) Profile of rifaximin and its potential in the treatment of irritable bowel syndrome. Clin. Exp. Gastroenterol. 8:159-167.

Lewis C. (2018) The Enlightened Mr. Parkinson: The pioneering life of a forgotten English surgeon. London: Icon.

Pearce JM. (2004) Thomas Addison (1793-1860). J. Royal Soc. Med. 97(6):297-300.

Reaven GM. (2005) Why Syndrome X.? From Harold Himsworth to the insulin resistance syndrome. Cell Metabol. 1(1):9-14.

Yudkin J. (2012). Pure White and Deadly. How sugar is killing us and what we can do to stop it. London: Penguin.

Websites

https://thiamine.dnr.cornell.edu

https://poisonousplants.ansci.cornell.edu

Acknowledgements

This book would not have been possible without the support of a large number of people – friends, family members and colleagues – and the following list is not exhaustive. For keeping me alive – Hugh Wilson, Emmanuel Huguet, Ewen Cameron, Filip van Tournout, Waldemar Bartosik and Nick Cheshire; seeing and advising me – Alison Prior, Peter Preston, Jane Collier, Nick Carroll, Simon Gabe; hearing my, at times, wild conspiracy theories – Mark, Hugh, Sophie, Catherine, Gill, John, Al and Mike; proofreading numerous editions – in particular, Catherine and Gillian Nash, also Claire Urwin; reading through and feeding back encouraging vibes – Philippe Grunstein, Alison Pagan, George Sergent, Nicky Leftley and Claire; being there and laughing during the good times and helping me through the difficult times – Mark, Catherine, Sophie, Freddie, Alex, Claire, Gill, John, Zaiga, George, Katharine Bundell and Jenny Huguet; correcting my attempts at Latin translation – Olive Angier; my fantastic editor and publisher, Danielle Wrate, and her team: Alexa and Abby, I would never have made it without their expertise; my patients and their stories – I miss working with patients; providing me with early inspiration and life mottos – Gillian Nash and Joan Coleman; standing by me through everything – Mark, my soulmate.

I am indebted to all those researchers who have worked valiantly, too many to name all, but in particular, John Yudkin, Gary Gibson and Derrick Lonsdale, who recognised the importance of thiamine, and believed that it could be used to treat a wide range of modern ailments. As I finish writing this, I find out that Gerald Reaven has died. He promoted the new concept of insulin resistance despite opposition. Until then only one type of diabetes existed, due to insulin deficiency. In 1988, he linked insulin resistance with the measurable abnormalities, such as raised cholesterol, that were associated with cardiovascular disease, and he is responsible for the term 'syndrome X'.

The names and features of my colleagues and patients have been altered.

About the Author

Jo trained in Southampton, Oxford and Cambridge as a General Physician and Gastroenterologist, before settling in Norwich as an Acute Medicine Consultant, where she worked for 10 years. She lives in Norfolk with her husband and four children, and until life took her in a different direction, forcing her to give up medicine, she was determined to have a family and a career.